THE LOCKHEED (BOEING / GENER
F-22 ADVANCED TACTICAL FIGI

The first of two Lockheed YF-22A prototypes to fly was N22YF, powered by General Electric YF-120 engines. The YF-22A gives the impression of being a relatively small aircraft, in fact, it is somewhat larger than the F-15. Noteworthy is small Skunk Works logo in white at base of vertical fin, just ahead of rudder.

DEDICATION:

This book is dedicated to my friend and colleague Erwin J. Bulban. His high technical standards and extraordinary moral character will forever remain a model to anyone aspiring to become a professional aerospace journalist.

CREDITS:

Unlike many of the books produced by Aerofax, Inc., this particular title, describing the most technologically advanced fighter in the world, is the end product of the efforts of Jeff Rhodes, a member of the public relations staff at Lockheed Aeronautical Systems Company's Marietta, Georgia facility, and Dick Abrams, Director of Flight Test for Lockheed Advanced Development Company (also known as the *Skunk Works*) in Sunland, California. Without their belief in their company's new fighter, their strong willingness to help, and their philosophical support, this book would not have been possible. Others who made significant and greatly appreciated contributions either directly or indirectly include Bob Tuttle of Lockheed Aeronautical Systems Company, Don Carson of Pratt & Whitney (special thanks), Tom Copeland, Dana Johnson of Texas Instruments, Tony Landis, Dick Martin of Lockheed Aeronautical Systems Company, John Pieper of Lockheed Aeronautical Systems Company, Mick Roth, James Sergeant of General Dynamics (special thanks), Ed Sexton of Revell/Monogram, and Richard Stadler of Lockheed Advance Development Company. Special thanks also to the Lockheed photographic team.

INTRODUCTION:

The requirement for a new air superiority fighter, simply acronymed ATF (Advanced Tactical Fighter) and codenamed *Senior Sky* by the Air Force, formally was identified during November of 1981 following approximately six months of Air Force promoted but industry subsidized study under a Request For Information (RFI) inquiry. By that date, many new technologies applicable to fighter design had begun to reach maturity in areas that included composite materials and lightweight alloys, advanced flight control system and avionics options, propulsion system upgrades, and low observables (stealth) technology. Concurrently it was projected that by the time the ATF

was being integrated into the operational service inventory all front-line Air Force and Navy fighters, including the McDonnell Douglas F-15 *Eagle*, the General Dynamics F-16 *Fighting Falcon*, the Grumman F-14 *Tomcat*, and the McDonnell Douglas F/A-18 *Hornet* would be nearing the end of their respective service lives.

Regardless of the latter, a detailed requirements definition and operational concept was developed after the November assessment. Though many of the responses to the RFI had envisaged multi-role aircraft, the resulting document focused on a clear need for an air superiority fighter specifically to replace the McDonnell Douglas F-15—and consequently capable of countering the sophisticated threats projected to exist during the early years of the next century.

During 1983, an ATF System Program Office (SPO) was formed under the aegis of the Aeronautical Systems Division (ASD) at Wright-Patterson AFB, Ohio. Col. Albert Piccirillo was assigned as the ATF SPO director and during September of 1983, concept definition study contracts were awarded to the seven manufacturers capable of producing a fighter to the evolving ATF specification. By the end of 1984, following some four initial drafts, the basic framework for the ATF requirement, calling for a radius of action of approximately 800 miles, supersonic cruise capability of Mach 1.4 to Mach 1.5, a 2,000 ft. runway requirement, a gross takeoff weight of 50,000 lb., and a unit cost of no more than $40 million in 1985 dollars was released to industry. Importantly, implied in the proposal was a requirement the ATF Life-Cycle Cost (LCC—aircraft unit cost upon delivery plus the cost of all spares, fuel, maintenance, and flying) be at least as good as,

if not better than, the McDonnell Douglas F-15.

During September of 1985, formal ATF Requests For Proposal (RFP) officially were solicited by the Air Force with the final submission date to be January of 1986. Differing little from the prototype drafts, it did lower the figure for the maximum unit cost from $40 million to $35 million, based on a buy of 750 aircraft at a total program cost (including full-scale development—or what now is referred to as engineering and manufacturing development) of $65 billion. The tight January deadline later was extended to April and concurrently, the Navy, under severe pressure from Congress, announced it would consider accepting a navalized ATF (NATF) as a Grumman F-14 replacement by the end of the 1990s decade.

Integral with the RFP was an initial perspective on what would soon become known as the Demonstration/Validation (Dem/Val) approach to prototyping. Initial studies leading to actual flightworthy aircraft would be accommodated at relatively modest cost by building full- and reduced-scale models for wind tunnel testing, radar cross section (RCS) computations, avionics development, and miscellaneous sub-systems testing. State-of-the-art capability in such sciences as computational fluid dynamics (CFD—utilized for extremely accurate wind tunnel assessments of analog hardware), RCS, and sub-systems test rigs interfaced with advanced computer capability greatly reduced the cost of what otherwise would be an extremely expensive full-scale prototype flight test program.

The concept exploration phase which started during 1983 involved Boeing, General Dynamics, Grumman, Lockheed, McDonnell Douglas, Northrop, and Rockwell International. It ran until the

The two Northrop YF-23A ATF prototypes, N231YF (87-800 — on the right) and N232YF (87-801 — on the left). Not now flying, they currently are being considered for acquisition by the NASA for use as research testbeds.

Aerofax, Inc. collection

General Dynamics model illustrating important YF-22A features, markings, and over-all planform.

Lockheed

Head-on view of YF-22A, N22YF, reveals subtle design features including upper wing surface camber, the extreme angularity of the various fuselage and intake external surfaces, and the root thickening at the vertical fin bases.

prototype contract awards were announced on October 31, 1986. In the interim, Grumman, known primarily for its Navy products and thus a political long shot, and Rockwell International, preoccupied with its B-1B problems and thus unable to devote the necessary logistical manpower required for a successful bid, eventually dropped out of the competition.

During May of 1986, Secretary of the Air Force Edward Aldridge announced a significant and important change in the original RFP. The Air Force had decided not to make its final ATF choice from the paper studies generated under the aegis of the original Dem/Val concept, but rather to expand Dem/Val and include a prototype fly-off that would pit the aircraft of the two most promising designs, those submitted by Lockheed and Northrop, against each other. Each contender would be asked to build two prototypes—each powered by examples of the two contending powerplant manufacturers.

Though considerably more expensive than the paper fly-off, the construction and flight testing of actual hardware—under the revised RFP—would permit a more accurate assessment of capabilities in the critical areas of low-observables technology and simple performance. Though up-front costs would be high, the long-term economics could almost certainly be justified by the resulting hardware revelations.

On July 28, 1986, the five remaining contenders submitted their prototype design proposals for analysis. During the following twelve weeks, these were reviewed with considerable intensity by ASD. It was concluded the Lockheed and Northrop program approaches were superior to those of Boeing, General Dynamics, and McDonnell Douglas. However, it also was concluded the three less desirable designs contained attributes applicable to the two preferred.

The five contending companies, under the duress of national economic realities and the Department of Defense, now elected to team in order to guarantee themselves at least a small part of the $65 billion pie that might result from an ATF production contract. Lockheed, whose initial design studies had been considered front runners during the early ATF reviews, initially had conducted consortium discussions with Boeing and General Dynamics as early as June of 1986, but did not formalize an agreement with its partners until the following October 13. Consequently, Lockheed assigned Sherman Mullin as General Manager for the ATF Team Program Office. He would direct Lockheed in the "prime contractor" role and consequently take advantage of the unique technical strengths of Boeing and General Dynamics. Northrop, some two weeks later, followed suit by serving as lead on a team with McDonnell Douglas.

These two consortia thus, by default, were selected on October 31, 1986 to build two prototypes each to compete in the revised Demonstration/Validation (Dem/Val) phase. Lockheed, under a $691 million contract, would build two of what later would become its Model 1132 aircraft under the official Air Force designation YF-22A and Northrop, under a similar $691 million contract, would build two of its design under the official Air Force designation YF-23A.

These aircraft, owned and operated by their respective consortia, later would be given civil registrations. The Lockheed YF-22As would be registered N22YF (powered by General Electric YF120-GE-100 engines) and N22YX (powered by Pratt & Whitney YF119-PW-100 engines), respectively.[1] The Northrop YF-23As would be registered N231YF (powered by Pratt & Whitney YF119-PW-100 engines) and N232YF (powered by General

---

1 The two Lockheed aircraft are at present expected to be transferred to the Air Force for tax and operational reasons.

Lockheed

As rolled out, the YF-22A prototype, N22YF was engineless. Sequencing of vertical fin tip markings, red at the top, white in the middle, and blue (with white stars) at the bottom, was reversed on aircraft N22YX. Additionally, N22YX carried the markings on the inside vertical tail surfaces; N22YF did not.

Electric YF120-GE-100 engines), respectively. The Northrop aircraft also were assigned military serial numbers, these being 87-800 for N231YF and 87-801 for N232YF.

Prior to this, a similar propulsion system competition had been initiated, pitting Pratt & Whitney against General Electric. The engine request for proposals (RFP), then referred to simply as the Advanced Fighter Engine (AFE) and later as the Joint Advanced Fighter Engine (JAFE) was released to the manufacturers during May of 1983. The following September, both were awarded $550 million contracts to build and test static prototypes. General Electric's engine was known in-house as the GE37 and Pratt & Whitney's as the PW5000. Later they would be designated F120 and F119, respectively, by the Air Force.

Initial preliminary flight rating tests (PFRT) and accelerated mission testing (AMT) runs using the prototype non-flightworthy engines took place during 1986 and two years later, the first flightworthy engines were bench run.

With the advent of the decision to prototype the two contending aircraft, the purpose of the revised Dem/Val phase was to focus on risk reduction and demonstrate that the advanced technologies required for successful accomplishment of the ATF's mission were feasible and practical and could be moved successfully into Engineering and Manufacturing Development (EMD). Dem/Val was composed of three major elements:

(1) System specification development, which utilized effectiveness analysis, design trade studies, tests, simulation, technology evaluations, and other efforts to refine the weapon system characteristics and operational requirements.

(2) Avionics prototypes, which were used to demonstrate the achievability of the fully integrated avionics suites, first in a series of ground based demonstrations, and then, for Lockheed, in the prototype Boeing 757 (N757A); initial tests took place on July 17, 1989), and for Northrop in a modified BAC 111 (N162W) modified as flying avionics laboratories (initial tests took place on July 17, 1989).

(3) YF-22A/YF-23A prototypes, which were used to demonstrate the capabilities on which the F-22/F-23 EMD proposals would be based.

With the Lockheed/Boeing/General Dynamics consortia, each company brought substantial, applicable experience to the partnership: Lockheed's experience in F-117A program design and production; Boeing's strength in military avionics development/integration and advanced materials development; and General Dynamic's expertise as designer and builder of the F-16 and its advanced fly-by-wire flight control system.

Northrop and McDonnell Douglas similarly were talented, with Northrop offering expertise in low-observables technology, lightweight fighter design (considerable data remained from the F-5 *Freedom Fighter* and F-20 *Tigershark* programs), and advanced materials technology; and McDonnell Douglas having experience in fighter design and fighter production.

The over-all distribution of work between the team partners was based on the dollar value of work performed, rather than on a man-hours to weight equation, etc. In simple terms, the program was divided into thirds for the Lockheed team and halves for the Northrop. This proved no simple task as interfaces required by these arrangements were extremely complex.

Lockheed's responsibilities included weapon system, air vehicle, and avionics system design integration, the forward fuselage (including the cockpit and air intakes), the wing leading edge flaps and tips, the vertical stabilizer leading edges and tips, the horizontal stabilator edges, and final assembly of the complete aircraft. Boeing's

A 1/12th-scale spin test model was one of many produced to accomodate studies pertaining to YF-22A aerodynamics. This particular model was equipped with adjustable control surfaces and a miniature spin chute assembly.

YF-22A, N22YF in final approach configuration. Noteworthy are extended flaps, a slightly drooped starboard aileron, and relatively flat pitch attitude. Pilot visibility forward is said to be excellent.

YF-22A, N22YF, apparently following its arrival at Edwards AFB, California at the end of its first flight. The pilot was Lockheed's Dave Ferguson. Noteworthy are static position of leading edge flaps, ailerons, and trailing edge flaps.

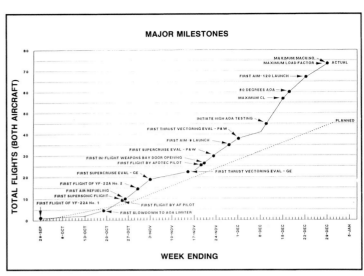

Lockheed

MAJOR MILESTONES

YF-22 FLIGHT DEMONSTRATION PROGRAM

Brig. Gen. James Fain (left); test pilot David Ferguson; Lockheed CEO Daniel Tellep; and Lockheed Dir. of Flight Test, Richard Abrams with YF-22A at end of first flight.

responsibilities included the wing, the aft fuselage, and propulsion system integration. General Dynamics' responsibilities included the mid-fuselage, the empennage, most subsystems, the armament system, the landing gear, and the vehicle management system integration (including flight controls).

Primary F-22 subcontractors totaled at some 650 scattered among 32 states. The most important of these included for Lockheed: Hughes Radar Systems Group, Los Angeles, CA (common integrated processor [CIP]); Harris Government Aerospace Systems Division, Melbourne, FL (fiber network interface unit [FNIU]; avionics bus interface [ABI]; fiber optic bus components [FOBC]; Fairchild Defense, Germantown, MD (data transfer unit [DTU] mass memory); GEC Avionics, Atlanta, GA (head-up display [HUD]); Lockheed Sanders Avionics Division, Nashua, NH (controls and displays; graphics processor video interface [GPVI]); Kaiser Electronics, San Jose, CA (unknown); Lockheed Sanders Information Systems Division, Merrimack, NH (mission planning equipment [MPE]); Lockheed Sanders Defense Systems Division, Merrimack, NH (common automatic test systems [CATS] software; and Digital Equipment Corporation, Merrimack, NH (systems/software engineering environment [S/SEE]).

For Boeing, the primary subcontractors were: Westinghouse Electric Corporation, Baltimore, MD and Texas Instruments Defense Systems and

A composite wing section for the YF-22A during assembly at Boeing Military Airplanes' facility in Seattle, Washington.

Electronics Group, Dallas, TX (radar); and Kidde-Graviner Ltd., Slough, UK (fire retardation equipment).

For General Dynamics the primary subcontractors were: Rosemount Aerospace Division (air data probes); Allied-Signal Aerospace Company [Bendix] and AiResearch Los Angeles Division, South Bend, IN (wheels and brakes); Curtiss-Wright Flight systems, Fairfield, NJ (leading edge flap driver system, side bay and weapons bay door drive); Dowty Decoto, Yakima, WA (hydraulic actuators); EDO Corporation Government Systems Division, College Point, NY (missile launchers); Lear Astronics Corporation, Santa Monica, CA (vehicle management system modules); National Water Lift Pneumo Corporation, Kalamazoon, MI (flight control actuators); Parker-Hannifin Corporation Parker-Bertea Aerospace Group, Irvine, CA (flight control actuator reservoirs); Simmonds Precision, Vergennes, VT (fuel management system); Sterer Engineering, Los Angeles, CA (nose wheel steering); TRW Avionics & Surveillance Group Military Electronic Avionics Division, San Diego, CA (communications and navigation equipment); XAR, City of Industry, CA (inflight refueling receptacle); Motorola, Scottsdale, AZ (computer security [KOV-5]); United Technologies Corporation Hamilton Standard Division, Windsor Locks, CT (environmental control system [ECS]); Sanders/General Electric Joint Venture Team, Nashua, NH (electronic combat equipment); Texas Instruments Defense Systems & Electronics Group, Dallas, TX (vehicle management system core hardware); and Menasco Aerospace Division, Ft. Worth, TX (nose/main landing gear).

Northrop and McDonnell Douglas's responsibilities were considerably different due primarily to the on-going work loads each company was able to accommodate. Accordingly, Northrop assimilated most of the design and engineering effort, the total systems integration, final assembly, construction of the aft fuselage and empennage, and defensive avionics and flight control system integration. McDonnell Douglas assimilated production of the forward and center fuselage, the landing gear and wings, the fuel and armament systems, the offensive avionics, the controls, and the cockpit displays. The crew station and pilot/vehicle interface were a joint responsibility.

By the advent of the roll-outs of the respective Northrop and Lockheed aircraft, the original 50,000 lb. gross weight limitation had been somewhat unwillingly shelved and a more realistic figure of 55,000 lb. had become the design goal. These weight problems had led to a number of

design changes that in turn led to delays in scheduling. For the Lockheed/Boeing/General Dynamics consortium, additional difficulties resulted in a diamond-shaped wing planform (its heritage being the General Dynamics Dem/Val proposal) supplementing an earlier, somewhat-less-tapered trapezoidal design. Additionally, the planform area of the forward fuselage was significantly decreased to provide improved high AoA (angle-of-attack) pitching moment forces in the low speed corner of the envelope. Extensive wind tunnel testing was undertaken to optimize the nose and vertical tail configurations in order to meet the AoA objective and generate optimum flying qualities.

Perhaps the most important change imposed on both the Lockheed and Northrop designs at this time was the elimination of engine thrust reversers. Originally an ATF design requirement, they had been studied in great detail by the various consortia members. The consensus was that their attributes would be offset by weight, maintenance, and cost considerations. Most importantly, full-scale testbed research had indicated considerable cooling difficulties and a propensity for the exhaust efflux to adversely affect directional stability when the reversers were used in flight. These anomalies would have necessitated design changes that would have affected the proposed ATF production schedule. Designed to operate throughout the ATF's flight envelope, the reversers would not have been simply an extrapolation of extant reverser technology, but rather a major technology risk—and thus an unknown quantity on an aircraft optimized for dependability and high performance.

ATF program management had, by now, been placed under the direction of Program Director, Brig. Gen. James Fain. Fain was quick to extend initial security constraints limiting access to the project, and accordingly, it was not until the roll-out ceremonies during 1990 that the prototype aircraft first were exposed to public scrutiny. In the interim, development and hardware construction by the two contending consortia centered upon three major groupings: the avionics ground prototype (AGP) which served as a static testbed for all avionics, sensors, and cockpit displays; the systems specifications development which accommodated RCS, materials, maintenance requirements, and simulated combat mission studies; and the prototype air vehicle (PAV) which called for the construction and flight test of the actual aircraft. The Northrop PAVs would be assembled at the company's Hawthorne, Califor-

4

Composite skin panel during through-transmission ultrasonic (TTU) testing at Boeing. Such testing provides a non-destructive means to ensure manufacturing quality.

Strips of thermoplastic-resin composites for a YF-22A wing panel. Such parts are at least as strong, and considerably lighter than their metal counterparts.

nia facility and then transported to Edwards AFB, California for roll-out and initial static tests; and the Lockheed PAVs would be assembled by Lockheed at their Palmdale ("Skunk Works"), California facility where they, too, would be rolled-out and put through initial static testing.

Four years after contract signing, the prototype ATFs were ready for flight. The first of these, Northrop's YF-23A, N231YF, was rolled out on June 22, 1990. It was followed on August 29, by the roll out of the first YF-22A, N22YF. The first of the new ATF prototypes to take to the air was again the Northrop aircraft, this occurring with the first hop of N231YF from Edwards AFB on August 27, 1990.

Northrop's flight test program progressed rapidly. The first inflight refueling was completed using 87-800 on its fourth mission on September 14th; it achieved a supercruise speed of Mach 1.43 on September 18; and its 34th and final flight took place on November 30, 1990. Total flight time logged utilizing 87-800 was 43 hours. The second YF-23, 87-801, first was flown on October 26; was supercruised for the first time at Mach 1.6 on November 29; and was flown for the last time on December 18. Total flight time logged utilizing 87-801 was 22 hours during 16 flights. YF-23 maximum speed achieved during flight test was 1.8 Mach and maximum altitude achieved was 50,000 ft. (15,240 m.).

YF-22A FLIGHT TEST PROGRAM:

The primary focus of the Lockheed half of the Dem/Val flight test program, under the direction of Lockheed's Richard Abrams, was on those objectives the contractor team felt would provide the Air Force with quantitative data that clearly demonstrated YF-22A performance capabilities directly relatable to the F-22A EMD design. A flight test strategy then was developed to use the prototypes to satisfy this objective by demonstrating the following capabilities: super maneuverability/controllability (sometimes referred to as agility); supercruise (i.e., supersonic cruise without the use of afterburner) with both engine options (i.e., Pratt & Whitney and General Electric); high AoA flight characteristics; live missile firing of both the AIM-9M *Sidewinder* and the AIM-120 Advanced Medium Range Air-To-Air Missile (AMRAAM).

In order to accomplish these specific test objectives in the limited time available, it was

mandatory that an efficient and aggressive test approach be utilized. This included: ensuring the required resources were available to support a high sortie rate; utilizing inflight refueling to the maximum extent possible; only conducting those envelope expansion tests that were absolutely required to demonstrate the specified performance capabilities; planning for, and utilizing multi-discipline test techniques; and early checkout of both the Air Force Flight Test Center (AFFTC) and Air Force Operational Test and Evaluation Center (AFOTEC) pilots and their full participation in the Dem/Val program.

For planning purposes it was assumed that ten productive flights per month per aircraft was a reasonable expectation for the Dem/Val program based on YF-16, YF-17, and F-117A experience. Based on the probability of nature's cooperation, government holiday and airshow schedules, and aircraft problems, etc., it was recognized there would be weeks when the aircraft would fly many flights, and there would be periods where flights would be infrequent. Manpower and resources, however, were available to support a minimum of two flights per day, six days a week.

The average flight duration was estimated to be 1.2 hours; 2.8 hours was the expectation with inflight refueling. The flight test strategy was based on early qualification of the YF-22As for inflight refueling, and inflight refueling was planned to be used on 80% of the test missions.

Flight testing of the YF-22A prototypes was con-

ducted at Edwards AFB by a combined test team made up of personnel from each of the three contractors along with representatives from the two engine companies, avionics suppliers, vendors, and the Air Force. Air Force representation included personnel from the AFFTC and the AFOTEC. Team composition was as follows: Lockheed Aeronautical Systems Co.—90 in engineering and administration; Lockheed Advanced Development Co.—65 in maintenance, quality assurance, material, and piloting; General Dynamics—45 in engineering, materials, and piloting; Boeing Military Airplanes—40 in engineering, maintenance, and quality assurance; Air Force (AFFTC and AFOTEC)—20 in engineering, maintenance, and piloting; General Electric—20 in engineering and field service; Pratt & Whitney—20 in engineering and field service. The total personnel committed to the test thus was 300.

The Lockheed consortium had the overall responsibility for the planning and execution of the YF-22A flight demonstration program. In a departure from standard AFFTC practice, the Flight Test Center's dual role during the ATF Dem/Val program was that of facilitator and to provide safety oversight, rather than performing in its traditional test manager role.

The overall flight test plan was developed by the contractor team. The engine manufacturers provided inputs to this plan for their propulsion system related test requirements. The only guidelines set forth by the Air Force were that the prototype air-

With windows faired-over, the prototype Boeing 757, N757A, has been utilized by the Lockheed ATF team as an airborne testbed for YF-22A avionics, radar systems, electronic warfare systems, and related technologies.

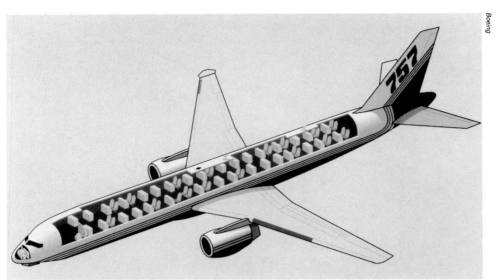

Simplistic cutaway of prototype 757 modified to serve as YF-22A flying avionics laboratory. This aircraft has permitted full-scale airborne testing resulting in reduced risk and lower projected development costs.

Pre-first flight view of N22YF at Palmdale. Noteworthy are extended leading and trailing edge flaps, nose chine, and open exhaust door for auxiliary power unit (mid-fuselage inboard of wing root).

Virtually all of the YF-22A flight test work was conducted over the Mojave Desert area around Edwards AFB. Noteworthy in this view of N22YF is its complex exhaust nozzle fairing assembly.

craft should be flown for the purpose of EMD risk reduction. The capabilities to be demonstrated during flight test were left to the discretion of the contractor team. Test planning documentation included the YF-22A Flight Demonstration Program Test Plan and supporting Test Information Sheets (TIS) for the following test disciplines: aircraft performance tests with the General Electric engines; aircraft performance tests with the Pratt & Whitney engines; handling qualities tests; General Electric engine tests; Pratt & Whitney engine tests; structural tests; flight systems tests; weapon systems tests; and crew systems tests.

The test plan review and approval cycle differed significantly from the norm for the Dem/Val program in that the AFFTC did not have approval authority. Therefore, there was no AFFTC test plan Technical Review Board (TRB) coordination, only that of the Safety Review Board (SRB). However, the ATF SPO did have review and approval authority for all of the flight test plans and they frequently looked to the AFFTC for their opinions regarding the plans.

Test mission control and real time telemetry monitoring was accomplished utilizing control rooms located in the AFFTC's Ridley Mission Control Center (RMCC). A telemetry relay van was used at Palmdale to assure good TM reception at the RMCC during engine runs, taxi tests, and first flights of both prototypes. In addition to Ridley, a control room with a limited capability to support real-time requirements was located in the YF-22A Combined Test Force (CTF) engineering complex. Because of its limitations, this facility could be used only to control benign test missions. The facility never was used to control a mission during Dem/Val, but it was used extensively to supplement (in a passive mode) the primary control room in the RMCC.

Data processing was accomplished at Lockheed's Palmdale Flight Test Data Center (FTDC) using either tapes from the airborne instrumentation system or TM data. Several analysis programs were available at the FTDC that were used to further process the data. Some of these were quite specific with regard to engineering disciplines whereas others were general in nature and used quite widely by all disciplines.

A secure, high-capacity network was used to link the Edwards AFB YF-22A CTF facility to Lockheed's Palmdale FTDC and Burbank plant, the General Dynamics Ft. Worth facility, and Boeing in Seattle. The network was utilized extensively by Flight Test for many purposes during the Dem/Val program. For example, the flight test data base housed in the Palmdale FTDC could be accessed from many of the other locations for detailed engineering examination and analysis. Flight control system OFPs also could be transmitted directly over the net from Ft. Worth to Edwards AFB, completely eliminating the necessity of having to ship discs or cassettes between the various team facilities. The net also was used frequently to transmit various types of flight test documentation such as test plans, reports, etc.

As noted previously, the purpose of the YF-22A Dem/Val flight test program was: to establish readiness for low risk EMD and to generate flight test data required for the EMD proposal and "sealed envelope" comparison. It was not for the purpose of determining the full capabilities of the YF-22A aircraft in the classic sense, nor to determine compliance with design requirements or specifications.

In some respects, therefore, the program had to be structured somewhat differently than a "normal" development flight test program. Both YF-22A prototypes were treated as the first of the type, not only because of the immaturity of the airframe, but because each was powered by different

Extreme close coupling of the horizontal stabilators and the wing trailing edge is readily apparent in this view of N22YF during flight test operations over Edwards AFB.

Pilot visibility fore and aft is exceptional in the YF-22A. Single-piece bubble canopy precedent was set by Lockheed ATF team member, General Dynamics, with F-16.

YF-22A, N22YF, with anti-spin chute assembly. Chute could be ballistically deployed in an emergency and could significantly improve spin recovery chances.

prototype engines (since the first Northrop YF-23A had flown with the Pratt & Whitney YF119 engines, it was assumed that by the first flight date of the No.2 YF-22A, the engine type had effectively already been flown).

Much of the testing intended to be accomplished on the first prototype was planned to be repeated on the second in order to obtain as much comparative data as possible with both engines. The first prototype was tasked with accomplishing the high AoA tests. The second YF-22A prototype was equipped with a stores management system (SMS) and missile launchers and it would be used for weapons bay environment and armament tests. From the beginning it was intended the AFOTEC would conduct their Early Operational Assessment (EOA) utilizing both aircraft. Each of the aircraft's planned test task assignments were then as follows:

Test Task Assignment	A/C-1	A/C-2
Initial Airworthiness	Yes	Yes
Limited Envelope Expansion (Flutter/Flying Qual./Loads)	Yes	No
Propulsion System Tests	Yes	Yes
Aerial Refueling Qualification	Yes	No
Supercruise & Performance	Yes	Yes
Maneuverability/Controllability	Yes	Yes
Weapon Bay Vibration & Acoustics	No	Yes
Live Missile Launches	No	Yes
High AoA Tests	Yes	No

Low and medium speed taxi tests were performed on both prototypes prior to their first flights. The primary objective of these tests were to evaluate ground handling characteristics, braking dynamics, the anti-skid system, longitudinal control capability, FLCC air data accuracy, nose wheel steering characteristics and to ensure there was

no landing gear shimmy or adverse interaction between the aircraft's structural bending modes and the flight control system. Secondary objectives were to assure that all onboard systems (including instrumentation) were operating normally in preparation for first flight. The only anomaly observed during these tests was an apparent bias of approximately 3° between the nose boom and the FLCC air data system AoA indications. FLCC AoA errors of as much as plus or minus 5° had been evaluated in the flying qualities simulator and the consensus of the pilots and General Dynamics flight control personnel was that this would not pose any particular flying qualities problem within the intended initial airworthiness flight envelope. The decision was made to fly with the bias and obtain inflight calibration data before attempting to correct it.

The first flight of the number one YF-22A, N22YF, powered by the General Electric YF120-GE-100 engines was made by Lockheed test pilot Dave Ferguson from Lockheed's Palmdale facility to Edwards AFB on Saturday, September 29, 1990. Flight duration was shorter than originally planned because the takeoff had been delayed while a ground station problem was rectified. The long static time on the ground consumed considerable fuel, and thus flight duration was affected.

The landing gear were not retracted during the first flight. It probably would not have retracted anyway, as difficulties with what the F-22 Program Manager termed ''Fascist Software'' prevented retraction until the fifth flight. As it turned out, the landing gear extension command was hardwired, but the retraction cycle was controlled by the integrated vehicle subsystem control (IVSC). Bypassing the IVSC landing gear retraction control with

independent hardwiring solved the problem.

Once the landing gear retraction anomaly was corrected, the pace of the flight test program increased rapidly. Initial tasks for N22YF were to complete its initial airworthiness tests in order to establish a reasonable level of confidence with the aircraft's flying qualities, performance, and engine and systems operation. Concurrently with the accomplishment of those objectives, the plan was to expand the flutter envelope clearance up to Mach 1.6 at 40,000 ft. (450 KEAS). This goal was achieved approximately one month into the program on the fourteenth flight of the aircraft. By this time, the KC-135 tanker qualification tests also had been completed. These all were flown by the AFFTC YF-22A project pilot, Maj. Mark Shackelford.

A short down time now followed permitting incorporation and checkout of a new FLCC operational flight program (OFP) that would enable the use of thrust vectoring. The spin recovery chute (SRC) also was installed and other modifications were made to the aircraft and FLCC software that eliminated the PADS AoA error. The bias was corrected by drooping the air data probes 5° and fine tuning the FLCC local flow angle corrections. Shortly thereafter, high AoA testing was initiated. The objective in this phase was to reach 60° AoA and be able to perform pitch and rolling maneuvers at this flight condition. This was accomplished in one week. The SRC was removed from the aircraft and the majority of test effort for the remainder of the Dem/Val program was devoted to supersonic envelope expansion along with performance, flying qualities, propulsion system and loads testing out to maximum speed.

The first flight of the second YF-22A, N22YX, was made by Lockheed test pilot Tom Morgen-

Few anomalies surfaced during the course of the somewhat abbreviated YF-22A flight test program. Pilots privileged to fly the two prototypes noted they were docile but very capable air combat platforms.

YF-22A, N22YF, turning final at Edwards AFB. Noteworthy are extended flaps, the main gear moving into their down-and-locked position, the open APU exhaust door, and the superb visibility afforded the pilot.

YF-22A, N22YF, in clean configuration but with anti-spin chute assembly in place. The chute could be pyrotechnically deployed. Though successfully tested, it was not required during the spin program.

YF-22, N22YF, in clean configuration. This was the General Electric YF120 powered prototype. Today it is permanently grounded and used for mock-up work at Lockheed's Marietta, Georgia facility.

feld on October 30, 1990. Once initial airworthiness testing was completed, the thrust of its program was directed toward the completion of all the prerequisite testing that was required prior to conducting a live AIM-9M *Sidewinder* missile launch. This task was completed approximately one month after first flight and the AIM-9M live launch was accomplished successfully on November 28, 1990. The AIM-120 AMRAAM live launch was accomplished just before Christmas, on December 20, 1990. The remainder of the second prototype's flight test program was devoted to supersonic envelope expansion along with performance, flying qualities, and propulsion system testing. The YF-22A flight test program was completed on December 28, 1990.

The primary focus of the YF-22A Dem/Val flight test program was to demonstrate the following capabilities:

(1) Super maneuverability and controllability with both the Pratt & Whitney and General Electric engines to include specific excess power, turning and rolling performance, and pitch response. Doublets, sideslips, rolls, and wind-up turns were used to evaluate the YF-22A's handling qualities. These data then were compared to wind tunnel and flight simulator results. Qualitative evaluations also were performed for the takeoff, landing, formation, and tracking tasks. Formation flight evaluations included air refueling as well as normal formation tasks. Lastly the effects of thrust vectoring, speed brake operation, and weapons bay door position also were evaluated.

In general there was very good agreement between the predicted and actual results. Handling qualities during takeoff and landing were found to be excellent. The landing evaluations included overhead approaches as well as straight in approaches from normal, high, low, and laterally offset starts. In addition, no problems of any kind were observed during simulated and actual single-engine approaches and landings. The crosswind landing envelope was expanded easily out to 20 kts. within five weeks of first flight.

Sustained load factor and specific excess power test results are classified. However, both of these performance parameters either met, or exceeded predictions. Rolling performance test results were less than predicted. At .90 Mach and 30,000 ft. the predicted full stick deflection roll rate was 200° per second; the flight test value was 180° per second. At 1.5 Mach and 40,000 ft. the predicted value was 185° per second as compared to the demonstrated value of 175°.

Flight test measured roll damping was higher than used in the FLCC control law design, and changing the control law gains to reflect the measured roll damping would increase the roll rate at .90 Mach.

At 1.5 Mach, adverse sideslip induced by the roll maneuver was larger than predicted in part due to the pneumatic air data system measuring AoA 1.5° lower than true. This resulted in incorrect aileron-rudder interconnect scheduling and excessive sideslip.

In the cruise configuration only one small problem was noted, that being a bit of excessive sensitivity to small roll inputs. That was corrected easily by a minor gain change. Formation flying and aerial refueling were accomplished easily, with level one handling qualities being exhibited throughout. As an example, the initial air refueling and subsequent boom envelope expansion were accomplished on the first two flights flown by Air Force test pilot Maj. Mark Shackelford.

The integration of thrust vectoring into the flight control system went very smoothly, beginning with the first thrust vectoring flight on November 15, 1990. This was in spite of the fact the two separate sets of control laws were required

YF-22A, N22YF in low-speed cruise configuration. Leading edge flaps are slightly displaced. Noteworthy is large root notch in flap for horizontal stabilator.

In response to ATF requirement, YF-22A is optimized to cruise at supersonic speeds without use of afterburner. Edwards AFB complex is visible just above nose of N22YF.

because of the two different airframe/engine combinations. Thrust vectoring was reported as being transparent to the pilot as far as handling qualities were concerned.

The increased performance gained through thrust vectoring was very evident both at high AoAs and in increased maneuverability at supersonic speeds. In fact, supersonic agility was widely praised by the pilots who likened the YF-22A when supersonic to other fighters when subsonic. In all, the YF-22A was judged by all of the pilots who flew it to be a very pleasant aircraft to fly.

(2) Supersonic cruise performance at intermediate thrust (supercruise) with both engine designs. Supercruise performance was evaluated with both the General Electric (achieved for the first time on November 3, 1990) and Pratt & Whitney engines (achieved for the first time on December 27, 1990), and the method of test was relatively straight forward. Actual temperatures aloft were obtained on the day of the flight from weather balloon data. These data then were used to estimate the predicted supercruise Mach number and altitude for the appropriate prototype aircraft. The aircraft then was accelerated using afterburner to the predicted supercruise flight conditions, the throttles were retarded to intermediate thrust, and the aircraft then was allowed to accelerate or decelerate (if required) in order to stabilize at the test day supercruise flight conditions.

The specific supercruise test results are classified, but, in general terms, the YF-22A proved quite capable of maintaining level flight in supersonic cruise conditions using intermediate thrust for as long as desired. This capability was demonstrated on several occasions during the Dem/Val program at altitudes between 37,000 ft. and 40,000 ft. A cruise in excess of 1.58 Mach was claimed by unofficial sources for the GE-powered aircraft and 1.43 Mach for the Pratt & Whitney. Between the two, a total of more than 4 hours at supersonic speeds was logged. From these test results it was concluded the YF-22A's supersonic installed thrust minus cruise drag (excess thrust) was as predicted.

(3) High AoA flight characteristics. Outstanding low speed agility was considered a hallmark of the YF-22A design. Therefore, early in the development of the Dem/Val flight test plan it was deemed appropriate to devote a relatively significant amount of the flight test effort to demonstrating the aircraft flight characteristics at lowspeed, high AoA flight conditions. Historically, however, high AoA flight testing has been full of surprises due to the complexities of predicting the results. For this reason, and the inherent hazardous nature of these tests, the test methods to accomplish this testing were thoroughly scrutinized before testing began on December 10, 1990.

As discussed previously, the YF-22A's flight control system was designed to utilize the engine

nozzles in the pitch axis. Pitch control, therefore, is provided by a combination of symmetric movement of the horizontal stabilators and thrust vectoring (TV). There are no flight control system AoA limits, and there is sufficient nose-up trim capability to permit trim flight at extreme AoAs. By utilizing thrust vectoring in the pitch axis, it was possible to reduce the area of the horizontal tail. But, it is still large enough to ensure there is adequate nose-down pitching moment capability to preclude the possibility of a deep stall at high AoAs with thrust vectoring off or in the event of a dual engine failure. Roll control is provided by a combination of ailerons, flaperons, and differential horizontal stabilator, with the rudders being used to coordinate the rolls. The additional pitch control available with thrust vectoring permits the FLCS roll rate limiter to be increased. This is due to the increased pitch capability required to counter inertially produced pitching moments in lowspeed rolls. It results in the pilot being able to generate significantly higher roll rates with thrust vectoring on as compared with the maximum roll rates with vectoring off.

The YF-22A spin recovery chute system design was similar to that used on the General Dynamics F-16 with the exception of the fact the YF-22A's empennage and exhaust nozzle configuration required the use of a larger quad-mount for the chute canister as compared to the F-16's tri-mount. The chute diameter is 28 ft. and the riser length is 100 ft. to ensure the deployment chute would be well outside the exhaust plume with the exhaust nozzle at its full trailing edge up position. Ground taxi (76 KIAS) and in-flight (165 KIAS @ 25,000 ft.) deployment and jettison tests were conducted prior to initiating the high AoA flight tests. There were no problems encountered during these tests nor was the chute ever used for recovery during the high AoA test program. Additional prerequisite testing included: flying qualities tests (1 g maneuver blocks) up to 20° AoA with thrust vectoring on and off....the maneuver block usually consisted of a trim point, pitch, roll and yaw doublets, sideslips, and bank-to-bank 180° and 360° rolls; engine airstarts; auxiliary power unit/ emergency power unit airstarts; and zero and negative g system tests.

The prerequisite testing was completed on December 10, 1990, just a little over two months after first flight. The actual high AoA test plan consisted of a methodical test matrix which allowed a careful evaluation of aircraft stability and control/handling qualities at progressively higher AoA. A typical high AoA maneuver block consisted of: a 1 g slowdown to the test AoA, trimming at that AoA and then pitch, yaw and roll doublets, rolling maneuvers, throttle transients (up to 40° AoA), and full forward stick pushovers.

All of the maneuvers were accomplished with thrust vectoring on and with the throttles set at intermediate (INT) thrust, except the 1 g pushovers.

The pushovers were accomplished first with vectoring on at INT thrust, and then repeated at idle thrust with vectoring off to determine basic aircraft pitching moment.

Real time comparisons of predicted versus actual maneuver results were used to issue clearance to the next test point. This procedure worked very well and was critical to the aggressive test schedule. All planned Dem/Val high AoA tests were completed in nine flights (14.9 hrs.) over a period of one week with the end of testing on December 17, 1990. These were the critical tests used to demonstrate basic aircraft aerodynamics, thrust vectoring, flight control system design, aircraft handling qualities, and to verify correct operation of the air data and inertial navigation systems.

The AoA build-up was accomplished in 2° increments from 20° to 40°, and in 4° increments from 40° to 60° (the change in this increment was due to an extremely small change in aircraft flight condition for a 2° change in AoA above 40°).

The pilots were very pleased with the aircraft's handling qualities at high AoA. Light airframe buffet was noted at 22° and increased slightly at 24°. The buffet intensity or frequency did not change after this point up to 60° and may actually have started to decrease. Of particular note was the precise pitch control at all AoA. Both pitch attitude and AoA could be held to within 1/2° with thrust vectoring on. With thrust vectoring off, control was less precise due to control law changes and the obvious loss of control power, and AoA could be maintained only to within 1° to 2°.

When the doublets had been completed at a given AoA, rolling maneuvers then were accomplished at a slightly lower AoA, usually 4° less. The absence of wing rock made precise and predictable rolling maneuvers possible. Rolling performance was very impressive. Roll response was immediate up to approximately 30° AoA and

YF-22A, N22YF, during infight refueling trials. Receptacle, closed here, is mounted on centerline.

YF-22, N22YF, repainted to resemble the Pratt & Whitney YF119-powered prototype, N22YX, during the June 1991 "Stealth Week" presentation at Andrews AFB, Maryland. Visible in the right background is the first B-2A.

YF-22A, N22YF, following its arrival at Lockheed's Marietta facility. Aircraft, which is now engineless, is being used as a mock-up to study EMD-specific systems and associated improvements.

then only hinted at the slightest delay at higher AoA. With aircraft N22YF, the test aircraft, there was a slight asymmetry between the left and right rolls. The left rolls were slightly faster, with less roll coast (rolling after the input was removed) and more AoA. As 30° AoA was approached, lateral trim requirements to maintain wings level began to increase. Above 30° AoA the trend then began to decrease and trim asymmetries at higher AoA flight conditions were negligible. This was observed in the cockpit as a slight increase in roll control activity but was not perceived as a noticeable

handling qualities deficiency. As AoA increased from 40° to 44°, roll control became slightly more sensitive and thus appeared to require more attention. Roll angle could be precisely controlled and deviations from wings level flight were less than 1°.

At 50° AoA, a phenomena that was observed in the flight simulator was confirmed in flight. At that AoA (in the simulator) pilots had noted a slight roll oscillation of plus or minus 5° that could be induced by small lateral stick inputs. This appeared to be caused by inputs that were made

faster than the aircraft could respond. This motion would quickly damp out if the stick was held frozen in the lateral axis, and with more careful inputs would not occur at all. Most were skeptical about the simulator's ability to predict this. Amazingly, it turned out to be a very accurate simulation, even at these extreme AoA. Aircraft roll response was always positive, and it was easy to hold the wings level for prolonged periods at these incredibly high AoA. Throughout the testing engine operation was excellent.

The high AoA program was very aggressive. Wind tunnel and simulator predictions were confirmed in a very complex portion of the envelope, while demonstrating the aircraft's outstanding high AoA capabilities. The YF-22A's high AoA handling qualities were best summarized by General Dynamic's test pilot Jim Beesley when he said, "It always did what I wanted it to do and never did anything that I didn't want it to do."

(4) Live launch of both an AIM-9M Sidewinder and AIM-120 AMRAAM. Internal weapons carriage was fundamental to the YF-22A's stealth characteristics and design and the team felt it was important to demonstrate live firings of both the AIM-9 and AIM-120 air-to-air missiles. The prototype aircraft were designed to carry air-to-air missiles in three bays; an AIM-9M in each side, or cheek bay (located aft of the engine intakes), and an AIM-120 in a central main weapon bay (located ventrally). Trapeze type launcher mechanisms were used to extend both missile types from the bays prior to launch.

The second YF-22A, N22YX, was utilized for the armament test program. Two of the three bays (left half and main) were fitted with launchers. A stores management system also was incorporated. Contrary to what one might expect to find in a prototype aircraft missile launch system (i.e. a pilot activated toggle switch that is hardwired to the launch mechanism), the YF-22A incorporated an essentially production type software-controlled stores management system (minus sensors).

Weapons bay vibration and acoustics tests were accomplished prior to the live missile firings. In the case of the AIM-120, these included the carriage of an instrumented missile to determine it's internal environment prior to carriage and launch.

Both missile firings were accomplished at .70 Mach and 20,000 ft. The AIM-9M test was conducted on November 28, 1990 at the China Lake Naval Weapon Test Center and was successful in all respects. The missile separated as predicted. There was no evidence of rocket exhaust impingement on the aircraft structure, nor engine exhaust plume ingestion.

The AIM-120 firing, which took place on December 20, 1990, also was an unqualified success. This test was accomplished utilizing the Navy's Pacific Missile Test Center range at Pt. Mugu. Missile separation and ignition was as predicted and it flew its intended trajectory.

All of these demonstration objectives were achieved in just over three months of flight testing.

The Air Force Operational Test and Evaluation Center (AFOTEC) participated in the YF-22A Dem/Val flight test program and conducted an early operational assessment (EOA) of the YF-22's capabilities with regard to its ultimate operational role.

Eleven flights were devoted to the AFOTEC EOA effort and a total of 13.9 hours were accumulated on both prototypes. All AFOTEC sorties were made up of tests extracted from approved test plans. However, the particular tests chosen for the EOA were more operationally oriented than typical engineering tests. For these evaluations the more tactical (as compared to engineering flight test) types of MFD display formats were utilized by the AFOTEC pilot.

YF-22A, N22YF, prior to its arrival at Marietta, was repainted with detail markings emulating those seen on N22YX. This effectively erased the fact that it had been powered by General Electric YF120 engines.

Jay Miller/Aerofax, Inc.

Lockheed

The Air Force fighter inventory of the future will effectively consist of the McDonnell Douglas F-15 (left), the Lockheed F-22, and the General Dynamics F-16.

YF-22A, N22YX, markings variations consisted of different YF-22 lettering, reversal of the vertical tail tip colors, and the change to a Pratt & Whitney logo.

At the conclusion of the Dem/Val program an independent assessment was prepared by the AFOTEC team and briefed by them up through the Tactical Air Command (TAC) chain of command. The YF-22A team's AFOTEC pilot, Lt. Col. Willie Naigle, stated the YF-22A was a "mighty fine machine at this phase of development."

Several unplanned tests also were accomplished during the Dem/Val program. The first of these was a wet runway landing at the end of the first flight. Thunderstorms had moved through the Antelope Valley area on the day of the first hop. Rain fell on the Edwards AFB runway a few minutes before the aircraft arrived for landing. Nothing unusual was noted by the pilot with regard to ground handling or operation of the brakes and anti-skid systems.

The first single-engine landing was accomplished on the third flight of N22YF following an inflight uncommanded shutdown of the left General Electric engine. The engine's control system logic had commanded the shutdown immediately after takeoff when an engine hydraulic system seal failed and all engine hydraulic fluid was lost. The aircraft's single engine flying qualities were judged to be excellent, and no special compensation on the part of the pilot was required for the subsequent landing.

To keep the competition between the engine manufacturers even, the first single engine landing on N22YX was made on its fifth flight following a precautionary shutdown of the right Pratt & Whitney engine when it was suspected that an air turbine starter had failed. The landing was uneventful even though it was General Dynamic's John Beesley's first flight in the aircraft.

The YF-22A's crosswind limit was raised to 20 kts. much earlier than planned when unforecasted high winds came up after N22YX had taken off on its third flight. The turbulence and crosswind posed no problems for the test pilot, Tom Morgenfeld.

The last unscheduled demonstration occurred on the eleventh flight of N22YF. This flight was terminated early due to the loss of fluid from the No. 1 hydraulic system following the failure of a pressure switch. The aircraft reacted to the loss of the hydraulic system as had been observed previously in the flight simulator and the return to the base and landing were accomplished by test pilot Maj. Mark Shackelford without any particular difficulty.

In early 1990, the ATF SPO had requested Lockheed to provide preflight predictions of various YF-22A performance characteristics against which they would be able to compare actual YF-22A test results determined from flight testing. The choice of parameters was left to the company. These preflight predictions were provided the SPO as the YF-22A "sealed envelope" performance during late June. These predictions were to serve as credibility criteria and as a "report card" to verify actual versus predicted performance.

The majority of the "sealed envelope" predictions and actual flight test results are classified, but the following provide general observations:

(1) Supersonic cruise was as predicted.

(2) Subsonic drags agreed at .90 Mach. In addition, the drag data obtained from both aircraft/engine combinations were in agreement with each other.

(3) Supersonic drags agreed at low lift coefficients. However, insufficient data was available at higher lift coefficients to make a valid comparison.

(4) Sustained load factors were as predicted.

(5) Specific excess power was as predicted.

(6) Based on flight demonstrations showing better acceleration performance than predicted, it was concluded the YF-22A drag rise and transonic drags were lower than predicted.

(7) Specific range at all test conditions was within 3% of predictions.

(8) Maximum speed was as predicted (and achieved on December 28, 1990).

(9) Maximum roll rates and time to specific bank angles at subsonic and supersonic cruise were less (and greater) than predicted, but judged to be quite satisfactory.

(10) Flying qualities at AoAs greater than 20° were judged to be excellent with thrust vectoring on, and acceptable with vectoring off. The ability to recover from any AoA was never in question.

(11) Flight measured buffet onset and CLmax were higher than predictions.

(12) Maneuver stability was close to predicted.

(13) Flying qualities were in the desirable and adequate range. However, some tailoring of the FLCC schedules or gains may be desirable to improve the ratings.

(14) Excellent engine/inlet compatibility was demonstrated with no throttle restrictions. No compressor stalls were experienced during the program.

(15) Engine operation was unaffected by AIM-9M and AIM-120 launches.

(16) Missile trajectories matched predictions.

(17) Weapon bay vibration and acoustic measurements showed good agreement with wind tunnel predictions.

(18) All airstart attempts were successful, with start times equal to or less than predicted.

(19) Measured stability derivatives were in good agreement with predicted values from wind tunnel data.

(20) No flutter was encountered, nor was it predicted to occur within the YF-22's full flight envelope.

(21) In general, the pneumatic air data system calibrations matched the wind tunnel predictions.

In the course of a three-month flight test program, the YF-22As were able to clear a demonstration flight envelope of over 7 gs, 82 KCAS to over Mach 2, and 50,000 ft. An aggressive flight test plan included the demonstration of supercruise capability with both the Pratt & Whitney and General Electric engines, flight control development (specifically thrust vectoring), demonstration of unequaled maneuverability across the airspeed spectrum from extremely low speed to high supersonic Mach numbers, and weapon separation from internal weapons bays. Despite the limited time available, all of these primary test objectives were accomplished without encountering any major snags.

From first flight of a new aircraft design to a cleared demonstration envelope in 91 days is an unequaled achievement in the modern history of aviation. Additionally, this was accomplished with two new engine designs and with the most advanced cockpit/avionics architecture ever flown in any fighter. Throughout this high intensity testing there was no foreign object damage (FOD) or safety incidents. Upon conclusion of the flight test program, 43 flights and 52.8 hours had been logged on N22YF and 31 flights and 38.8 hours had been logged on N22YX.

After a three-month-long review of the Dem/Val results and the associated EMD proposals from both Northrop and Lockheed[2], on April 23, 1991, Secretary of the Air Force Donald Rice announced that the Lockheed, Boeing, and General

2   Lockheed's EMD proposal was approximately 20,000 pages long and weighed approximately 4,500 lb. It was flown to Wright-Patterson AFB, Ohio aboard a specially chartered Convair transport on December 31, 1990.

Lockheed

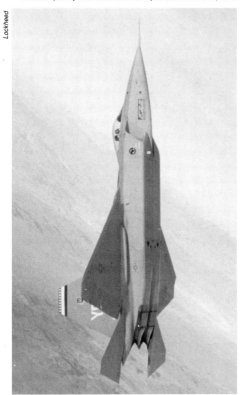

YF-22A's thrust-to-weight ratio is well in excess of 1 to 1 — thus permitting exceptional performance.

Lockheed

YF-22A PROTOTYPE PROGRAM HIGHLIGHTS

ACCOMPLISHMENT	A/C NO.	FLT NO.	DATE (1990)
First Flight of A/C No. 1			29 Sep
First Supersonic Flight	1	9	25 Oct
First USAF Piloted Flight	1	10	25 Oct
First Aerial Refueling	1	11	26 Oct
First Flight of A/C No. 2			30 Oct
Aerial Refueling Qualification Completed	1	12	31 Oct
First Supercruise Demonstration - GE	1	14	3 Nov
First Thrust Vectoring Evaluation - GE	1	15	15 Nov
First AFOTEC Piloted Flight	1	19	19 Nov
First Engine Airstart	2	6	20 Nov
First In-flight Weapons Bay Opening	2	6	20 Nov
First Supercruise Demonstration - P&W	2	8	23 Nov
AIM-9M Sidewinder Missile Launch	2	11	28 Nov
First Thrust Vectoring Evaluation - P&W	2	12	1 Dec
High Angle of Attack Testing Begins	1	28	10 Dec
28 deg Demonstrated	1	31	12 Dec
32 deg Demonstrated	1	34	14 Dec
36 deg Demonstrated, (C_L Max)	1	35	15 Dec
40 deg Demonstrated	1	36	15 Dec
44 deg Demonstrated	1	37	17 Dec
60 deg Demonstrated, Testing Completed	1	38	17 Dec
AIM-120 AMRAAM Missile Launch	2	24	20 Dec
Maximum Speed (greater than Mach 2)	1	43	28 Dec
Maximum Positive g (over 7.0)	1	43	28 Dec
Flight Test Program Complete			28 Dec

YF-22A, N22YX, was the Pratt & Whitney YF119-powered prototype. The only major physical difference was in a slight variation to the exhaust nozzle design.

Dynamics consortium had been selected to proceed with the EMD F-22A. At the same time, the Pratt & Whitney YF119-PW-100 engine was selected as the preferred powerplant. Rice noted the Lockheed and Pratt & Whitney designs "clearly offered better capability at lower cost, thereby providing the Air Force with a true best value".

The superiority of the Lockheed and Pratt & Whitney designs was attributed to their higher ratings on their technical proposals and their respectively better program management plans. Additionally, an Air Force assessment of risk led it to believe the Lockheed and Pratt & Whitney designs were more likely to accomplish their proposed objectives and that management would be more effective. It also was stated that cost differences, though slight, favored the Lockheed and Pratt & Whitney designs.

Northrop's YF-23A's had logged a total of 50 sorties over a 104 day period and had demonstrated a combat surge capability of six missions in ten hours (with eighteen minute turnaround times that included refueling and missile and gun rearming). The aircraft had demonstrated a 25°

AoA capability (though wind tunnel testing indicated a 60° capability without thrust vectoring) and had cruised supersonically at between 1.4 and 1.6 Mach for a total of 7.2 hours.

EMD:

As of this writing, Lockheed has revealed plans to resume flight testing of the second YF-22A, N22YX (the Pratt & Whitney powered prototype). This aircraft took to the air for the first time since the fly-off on October 30, 1991, piloted by Tom Morgenfeld. This follow-on work will take place at Edwards AFB and will consist of an additional 100 hours of flying time (approximately 25 flights) to expand the flight envelope and explore select envelope segments in greater detail. Approximately ten flights will explore additional air loads data at high-g with the weapons bay doors open and closed. Additional flights will explore the low altitude/high speed envelope, flutter testing, high AoA in maneuvering flight, and load measurement work. Additional missile launch trials also will be undertaken.

The first YF-22A, N22YF (the General Electric

powered prototype) has been flown to Lockheed's Marietta, Georgia facility where it will be used as a full-scale mock-up for EMD systems and hardware integration. It now has been repainted to externally echo the markings seen originally on N22YX—and it bears a Pratt & Whitney logo on the intake cheeks, accordingly. Additionally, the General Electric engines used to power this aircraft have been removed and the engine bays have been left empty.

One month later than originally planned, on August 3, 1991, the Air Force signed contracts totaling $9.55 billion with the Lockheed consortia and $1.375 billion with Pratt & Whitney consummating initial agreements leading to the manufacture and flight test of nine single-seat, two two-seat, and two fatigue and static test EMD aircraft. Pratt & Whitney will furnish 33 F119-PW-100 engines for the flightworthy aircraft. Fabrication of the first EMD F-22A aircraft, following freezing of the external design during October of 1991, is to begin during December of 1992 at Lockheed's Marietta facility. Assembly of the last of the EMD aircraft now is tentatively scheduled for late 1996

Lockheed

The YF-22A can appear graceful and attractive from certain angles — while sometimes resembling other operational fighters such as the McDonnell Douglas F-15.

YF-22A PROTOTYPE FLIGHT TEST PROGRAM STATISTICS

EVENT	YF-22A No. 1	YF-22A No. 2	Total
First Flight	9-29-90	10-30-90	—
Total Flights	43	31	74
Total Flight Hours	52.8	38.8	91.6
Total Contractor Flights	26	21	47
Total USAF Flights	17	10	27
AFFTC	14	2	16
AFOTEC	3	8	11
Most Flights Per Week	10	5	15
Most Flights Per Day	2	2	4
Average Flights Per Week	3.3	3.4	—
Total Pilots Checked Out			5
(2 LADC, 1 GD, 2 USAF)			
Air Refueled Flights	19	17	36
Missile Launches	—	2	2
Flights Per Month			
September	1	—	1
October	12	1	13
November	12	10	22
December	18	20	38

YF-22A wing, horizontal tail, and intake upper lip leading edge sweep angles are virtually identical — partly as a result of low observables requirements.

YF-22A, N22YX, slightly nose-high, in level flight. Large size of vertical tail surfaces and rudders are accentuated in side profile views such as this.

or early 1997 and will be followed by four pre-production verification F-22As. The latter will be used in operational Air Force tests and then introduced into the operational inventory. Full production of the F-22 is scheduled at this time to begin during late 1997 or early 1998.

Lockheed's Marietta, Georgia plant, as these words are being written, currently is in the middle of building an advanced 190,000 ft.³ robotic-optimized facility inside its 3,500,000 ft.³ primary B-1 production building to accommodate the sophisticated manufacturing techniques and equipment that will be required to produce the F-22A. A 138,000 ft.³ addition to the company's Adhesive Bonding plant in Charleston, South Carolina, where much of the company's share of the F-22A will be fabricated, presently is under construction, and new paint and fueling facilities are to be built at Marietta as well.

At the Marietta facility, all parts and subassemblies will be brought together in the southwest corner of building B-1. The F-22A area will be fenced off from other production areas (such as that producing the C-130 *Hercules*) primarily because select F-22A parts are classified.

ATF assembly will be simplified through the use of an automated track system. As the cockpit sections are built up, the track system will take the sections to the next work station. The completed cockpit sections will then move to another work station where the nose will be mated with the mid and aft fuselages. Once each fuselage can stand on its landing gear, the aircraft will be moved off the track. The wings and empennage then will be added.

The completed aircraft will go through final assembly and then be towed around the front of building B-2 to the flight-line area for fueling, painting, and radar cross section testing. Much of the delivery preparation will be done in buildings B-88 and B-89.

At the peak of EMD efforts during mid-1994, the F-22 team is expected to number approximately 7,000 employees at the three companies. The effort also will involve 650 suppliers in 32 states.

A go-ahead by the Air Force for F-22A low rate initial production is scheduled for 1996. The Air Force, though originally touting a buy of as many as 750 aircraft, now has settled on a figure of 648 in response to newly unveiled plans for force structure cutbacks scheduled for the mid-1990s. After production start-up during 2000, production rates are tentatively scheduled to peak at 48 aircraft per year during 2003 (after building up through 4, 12, 24, and 36 aircraft yearly) with total program costs estimated to be $98 billion ($18 billion for research and development and $80 billion for production) by the time the last order is consummated during 2012 and the last aircraft is produced during 2015. If the full complement of 648 aircraft is acquired,

it will equate to 5.5 tactical fighter wings (out of a proposed mid-1990s total of 26 tactical wings).³

First flight of the first EMD F-22A (Lockheed Model 639) is scheduled for mid-1995 with EMD work to continue through 1999. The contract delivery dates for the flyable EMD aircraft are at present: #4001, July 1995; #4002, December 1995; #4003, June 1996; #4004 (2-seat), August 1996; #4005, December 1996; #4006 (2-seat), March 1997; #4007, June 1997; #4008, September 1997; #4009, December 1997; #4010, February 1998; #4011, July 1998.

As of this writing, Navy interest in the navalized F-22, referred to as the NATF, has considerably diminished—though at one time as much as $8.5 billion was to be spent on prototype design and development. The F-22 Dem/Val program, however, provided approximately $1.2 billion in NATF technology transfers and generated some convincing arguments in favor of a navalized variant. Among the latter was a predicted 40% savings over a "stand-alone" Navy program. Additional life cycle savings were to have been generated through common F-22/NATF systems.

NATF production initially called for as many as 546 aircraft. This subsequently was reduced to 384 aircraft, and then to zero when the program was effectively cancelled. As of this writing, an option for program restart exists during the post-1997 period.

The NATF differed considerably from the Air Force F-22. Though utilizing many F-22 primary components, it would be designed from the "deck up" for carrier suitability. Lockheed claims to be in a position to produce up to four Navy F-22s per month if the service reverses itself and elects to move ahead with acquisition.

Though little concerning the exact physical characteristics of the NATF has yet surfaced in the public domain, artist's renderings indicate some commonality in the forward fuselage and empennage sections and virtually everything else being indigenous to the Navy requirement. The most striking difference is the addition of a totally new, variable-geometry wing and all-new horizontal and vertical tail surfaces.

Additionally, because of the multi-role (Combat Air Patrol [CAP]/strike escort) mission assigned to the NATF, it will carry a significantly different weapon system and associated weapon system sensor complement. Resulting from the latter will be a considerably different lower nose configuration with an integrated low observables-optimized sensor fairing.

Range, loiter time, and such ATF fundamentals as low observables technology and supercruise

---

³ The cost-plus-award-fee contracts allow reimbursement of contractors' costs plus a base fee of 4% of the estimated cost of the contract. Also included is the potential for a fee of an additional 9% above the estimated cost, based on contractor performance. A spending limit on the EMD phase has been set at $12.7 billion.

capability all would be different for the NATF in consideration of its mission. And because of aircraft carrier weight, launch, and landing constraints, the NATF's landing gear would be considerably stronger and heavier than those of the ATF.

CONSTRUCTION AND SYSTEMS:

Information applies specifically to the YF-22A unless otherwise noted.

General: Four major classes of advanced composite materials have been used on the YF-22A, demonstrating the contractor teams' ability to design and manufacture parts from wet and dry thermoplastics as well as bismaleimide (BMI) and epoxy thermoset materials. Examples of the use of thermoplastics on the YF-22A are the single-piece wing skins. The various materials used in the construction of the YF-22A prototypes consisted of graphite thermoplastics (13%); thermosets (10%); aluminum (33%); advanced aluminum alloys (2%); titanium (24%); steel (5%); and other miscellaneous materials (3%). The EMD F-22As will differ in being of aluminum (11%); titanium (33% [Ti 6-4, 11%; Ti 62222, 22%]); steel (5%); composites (35% [thermosets, 20%; thermoplastics, 15%]); and other miscellaneous materials (16%).

Composite materials are combinations of two or more organic or inorganic materials. One material serves as a matrix; the other serves as a reinforcement in the form of continuous fibers, dispersed in the matrix in an appropriate pattern. The function of the matrix is to bond the reinforcement together and to transfer loads between the fibers. The reinforcement supports the mechanical loads that the composite structure is subjected to in service.

Organic composite structural laminates are made up of stacks of oriented thin lamina that are consolidated under heat and pressure. Each lamina consists of a layer of high-strength, high-modulus, low-density reinforcing fibers embedded in a resin matrix. Fibers typically are materials such as carbon, boron, Kevlar 49, or fiberglass. The matrix can be either a thermosetting material such as epoxy, bismaleimide, or polyimide, or a thermoplastic material. If the matrix is thermosetting, a solid material is formed that cannot be reprocessed. Thermoplastic materials, however, can be reshaped by reheating and reforming.

Organic matrix composite parts currently being used on aircraft primarily are made up of thermoset materials that have been developed over the past twenty years. Thermoplastics for aerospace applications were introduced only a few years ago. An optimum mix of thermosets and thermoplastics has been utilized on the YF-22 and

YF-22A, N22YX, during inflight refueling trials, apparently over the Pacific Ocean.

will be utilized on the F-22 through complementary structural applications of each material class. In a program under contract to the AFSC, the Lockheed ATF team built 12 main landing gear doors for the General Dynamics F-16 using thermoplastics and advanced processing. In a second phase of this program, the team is producing three generic fighter center fuselage sections while establishing and verifying various manufacturing methods that include filament winding, press forming, thermal forming, pultrusion, and adhesive bonding.

The external shape of both prototypes and the EMD series aircraft has been optimized for low RCS. The blended wing/body configuration, which helps reduce RCS, also is structurally efficient and provides considerable internal volume for fuel carriage. Lockheed approached the complex problem of low observables from a systems engineering perspective. Requirements were established based on the mission, then a configuration was developed to satisfy the requirement. Configuration considerations included perimeter edge orientation and empennage interactions.

Additionally, low observable design efforts focused on subsystem performance. The engine intake/duct system, for instance, was required to balance low observables performance with propulsion system efficiency. Lockheed used an intake/duct design which provided low observables performance without requiring special, low observables engine compressor face designs (which typically have had a severe impact on the engine's installed thrust).

Fuselage: The fuselage, like much of the rest of the aircraft, is of mixed materials construction. Heavy emphasis has been placed on low observables technology, however, and accordingly, the metal components are covered with radar absorbent materials (RAM) and radar absorbent paint.

The fuselage is essentially modular in construction and is designed to provide maintenance access wherever possible without the use of ladders or access stools. Two large avionics bays are located in the fuselage nose section, these accommodating more than 100 common avionics modules in a liquid cooled chassis. Each module is individually replaceable in the event of failure.

Cockpit: The YF-22A's cockpit was designed to permit greater situational awareness through an excellent field of view while minimizing pilot workload through the use of colored liquid crystal (LCD) multifunction displays (MFDs) with finger-on-glass (FOG) controls. LCDs permit lower weight, lower power requirements, reduced volume, and improved performance.

The LCDs used in the YF-22 involve active matrix technology for the presentation of real-time video or graphic images. The displays have a contrast ratio in excess of 12:1 in a 10k foot lambert environment and a brightness of white in excess of 200 foot lambert. A single display is packed into two line replaceable units (LRUs), the remote electronics unit (REU), and the display unit (DU).

There are two 6 in. x 6 in. primary multifunction displays (PMFD) and three 4 in. x 6 in. secondary multifunction displays (SMFD). The primary MFD and secondary MFDs are full-color liquid crystal units.

In the EMD aircraft, the PMFD is used for the display of tactical information. The left and right SMFDs are for presentation of attack and defensive displays, respectively. The SSDs are for presentation of aircraft subsystem and stores management displays and checklists. The UFCD is for presentation of communications, navigation, and identification (CNI) data as well as caution, warning, and advisory messages. The HUD presents primary flight reference, weapon-aiming, and release information. Backup flight performance information is provided on a full-time basis by the standby flight group (SFG).

The pilot's ability to assess and manage the tactical situation and to prosecute the attack is enhanced by automation of sensors, threat assessment, and attack management tasks. This relieves the pilot of many routine tasks and provides the decision aids and situation awareness needed to maintain the advantage over an adversary.

The caution warning and advisory system is designed to eliminate indications that lead to a proliferation of unwanted and unneeded warning lights. Messages are displayed on the up-front control/display unit and are backed up by a voice annunciation system. The pilot is not only informed of what is wrong, but also is presented with the corrective actions required.

The hands-on throttle and stick scheme (HOTAS) allows the pilot to prosecute an attack from beyond-visual-range (BVR) to a one-on-one "dogfight" without having to remove his hands from the stick or throttles to manage offensive and defensive sensors and weapons. The integrated throttle control also provides the pilot with a single grip for control of both engines. Tailoring the throttle grip provides a comfortable hand rest and easy HOTAS switch manipulation. Auxiliary controls for independent management of each engine also are provided.

The cockpit is sized to accommodate 99% of the Air Force pilot population and is arranged to provide the pilot with a safe, comfortable working environment. Required controls and displays are within comfortable reach and view.

The single-piece laminated acrylic transparency on production aircraft will be chemically optimized to meet the F-22A's low RCS specification. The canopy frame is hinged at the rear and opens vertically via a single hydraulic ram.

There are no conventional round dial gages or engine instruments in the cockpit. All information is presented to the pilot via MFDs and the holographic HUD (which serves as the primary flight "instrument" for the aircraft; it is designed to be replaced without boresighting). The following types of display formats can be presented on the primary MFDs (Nos. 1, 2, and 3): vertical situation display; horizontal situation display; flight test display; equipment status display; and memory examine display.

The EMD aircraft cockpit will differ somewhat from the prototype but will have a side-stick controller, contrary to earlier plans calling for a conventional center stick. It also will utilize a modified (with leg and arm restraints and an advanced sequencer to reduce the chance of injury during ejections occurring above 450 kts) Weber ejection seat in place of the articulated ACES II seat found in the prototypes. The latter, with a pivot mount near the top of the seat, is an electronically interfaced unit designed to automatically rotate for and aft (along with the rudder pedals) in response to airframe g-loads—and thus increase pilot g-tolerance during maneuvering.

The development of a new tactical life support system (TLSS) flight suit and associated equipment apparently has offset the need for the articulated seat. The TLSS provides increased protection against high-g by providing both an upper and lower-body g-suit and a positive pressure breathing system. Chemical and cold water immersion protection is provided by the same garment. Comfort is aided by a personal thermal control system to control air temperatures from the environmental control system.

EMD aircraft will utilize a considerably different MFD control arrangement. Difficulties with the FOG system, due primarily to a lack of tactile feedback, have led to a decision to return to a conventional push button switch system around the screen bezels.

Under what is referred to as a "Federated" system, the avionics, including the radar, the IRST, the threat receivers, the communications/navigation/identification, weapons system, miscellaneous aircraft systems, and countermeasures system all feed into a 1 megabyte-per-

Serrated edges of landing gear doors, weapons bays, exhaust nozzle fairings, and other such items are physical concessions to low observables requirements.

With gear down and locked, YF-22A, N22YX is seen on October 30, 1990, on what apparently was its first flight. Lockheed pilot Tom Morgenfeld was the pilot.

The two YF-22As, N22YF (left) and N22YX in formation flight. Noteworthy are differences in YF-22 lettering on vertical fin, and reversal of fin tip colors.

The two YF-22As, N22YX (top) and N22YF in formation flight. The two essentially were identical except for engines and exhaust nozzle assemblies.

second serial bus.

The F-22 electronic combat suite combines multiple functions to counter advanced radars and long-range, multispectral weapons. The suite includes a radar-warning receiver, missile approach warning, infrared and RF countermeasures and electronic support measures functions. A precision direction-finding capability will aid situational awareness. All of these functions are contained on about 70 Standard Electronics Model E (SEM-E) format modules which fit together with a central integrated processor (CIP) computer being developed by the Hughes Aircraft Radar Systems Group.

On the prototype aircraft, the left primary MFD (No.1) can be removed when required and replaced either by a flutter excitation system panel or stabilization recovery chute control panel. The right primary MFD never has been installed. Instead, a special programmable cathode ray tube (CRT) display is installed and serves to provide flight test nose boom air data information. Four different types of display format can be selected by the pilot, depending on the type of testing being performed.

The secondary MFDs (Nos. 4, 5, and 6) are used to present the following types of display formats: subsystem status display; fuel status display; stores management display; and subsystem control display. For communication/navigation/identification the following are displayed: communication option page; TACAN option page; IFF option page; and INS option page. For head up and vertical situation displays the following are displayed: HUD declutter page and VSD declutter page. For integrated flight/propulsion control the following are displayed: engine controls page and flight test aid page. For mission data base the following are displayed: communication list page; TACAN list page; and waypoint list page. The flight test aid page enables the pilot to: select different pre-programmed control law options; perform automatic pitch, yaw, or roll doublets; adjust the load factor times weight (NzW) limiter to various percentages of the maximum allowable; and vary exhaust nozzle area ratio and nozzle trim angle.

The electronics and software that make up the prototype avionics suite for the YF-22A began flight tests on April 18, 1990 from Boeing's Seattle, Washington facility. A four-month check-out was undertaken utilizing Boeing's 757 Avionics Flying Laboratory (AFL) test aircraft. Prototype YF-22 sensors flown aboard the AFL included the Texas Instruments/Westinghouse active array radar, the TRW communications/navigation/identification system, the Lockheed Sanders/General Electric electronic combat system, and the General Electric infrared search-and-track unit.

The AFL, during the course of tests, was flown against targets of opportunity including commercial, general aviation, and military aircraft. Individual tests were used to evaluate the installed performance of each sensor, the integrated avionics suite, and the mission avionics sensor management and sensor track integration functions.

The flight control system, developed by General Dynamics, is a full fly-by-wire system. Development began during 1987 and involved about 60 employees at its peak. General Dynamics participated in decisions concerning the sizes and shapes of control surfaces, the types of control surface actuators, and the degree of maneuverability needed to accommodate the ATF's mission objectives. Additionally, the company's flight control engineering team participated in the wind tunnel test program and designed the aircraft's control laws.

A quadruple digital flight control computer (FLCC) configuration was chosen for the YF-22A primarily to take advantage of simpler redundancy management techniques. The FLCC output to the surface actuators is triple-redundant. Command signals to the flight control computers are initiated by applying position or force commands to the throttles, sidestick controller, or rudder pedals. These signals are processed by the flight control computers along with data from the air data sensors, rate gyros, and accelerometers.

Fly-by-wire is required in part because the F-22 utilizes longitudinal relaxed static stability. It also has automatic structural load limiting that permits the use of maximum allowable load factors throughout the flight envelope.

The cockpit is environmentally controlled and equipped with an on-board oxygen generation system (OBOGS) which manufactures oxygen to meet pilot requirements.

Wings: The wing is a titanium multi-spar design utilizing composite sub- and surface structures and materials. Thermoplastics have been utilized in the prototypes, but studies currently are underway exploring a less expensive thermoset alternative. Each wing is equipped with a single trailing edge aileron outboard and a large, single-piece flaperon inboard. The leading edge flap is also a single piece unit and extends to the wingtip.

The wing section is approximately 3.8% and is optimized for transonic operation. Some blending at the root section accommodates both RCS and aerodynamic requirements without compromising either.

Roll control is provided by a combination of differential movement of the ailerons, flaperons, and horizontal stabilators. Symmetrical movement of the full-span leading edge flaps, ailerons, and flaperons is scheduled as a function of AoA, Mach number, and landing gear position. All control surfaces are hydraulically actuated. All surfaces droop during low-speed flight to accommodate lift requirements in that part of the envelope.

Tail Surfaces: The horizontal and vertical tails, with metal load bearing structures and composite skins, have been designed to provide unrestricted maneuvering and battle damage redundancy. Pitch control is provided by symmetrical movement of the horizontal stabilators and engine nozzles. It has been proposed that production F-22As utilize vertical tails made of metal-matrix composites (MMC). The rudders provide directional control and coordinate the aircraft in rolls.

Landing Gear: The tricycle landing gear is conventional in layout and design. All three gear retract forward via independent hydraulic ram-type actuators. Each main gear wheel is equipped with a dual anti-skid disc brake assembly. Each main gear well is covered by a single piece door. The nose gear well is covered by a two-piece door. RCS considerations dictated the design of the forward edge of the main gear door panels.

An F-15-style, hydraulically actuated speed brake is located between the vertical stabilators, aft of the inflight refueling receptacle. It is hinged at its forward end. Lockheed, as of this writing, continues to explore alternatives to this configuration permitting its elimination and is contemplating the use of rudder "snowplowing" as one option.

Powerplant: Two different engine designs, one by Pratt & Whitney and one by General Electric were tested on the YF-22A prototypes. Both were capable of self-starting, and both were equipped with autonomous ground checkout systems. Design objectives were centered on very high thrust-to-weight ratios and high reliability.

For Pratt & Whitney, initial development in a dem/val program sponsored by the ASD began during 1983. During 1984, component rigs were designed and models were tested; during 1985 the demonstrator engine design was completed, the component rigs were fabricated, and testing was initiated; during the 1987-1989 time period additional component core and engine testing was undertaken; and during 1989, the first flight test work was initiated using prototype engines.

In the YF-22/F-22, the powerplants are fed by separate fixed ramp, wedge-shaped intakes. These provide low distortion air to the engines while also providing a high recovery rate. Low observables requirements played a preeminent role in the intake design and the resulting configurations provided 100% line-of-sight blockage to the engine face—and thus all but eliminated return energy leaks. On the EMD aircraft, the intakes will be somewhat farther aft, thus giving the aircraft a different forward fuselage profile.

The intake tunnels are provided boundary layer bleed systems which dump air through covered slots located just behind the upper intake lip. The auxiliary intakes also are mounted dorsally.

When the Pratt & Whitney YF119-PW-100 was selected as the ATF propulsion system winner over the General Electric YF120-GE-100, the long-term production potential for the engine equated to some 1,500 units with production to be initiated during 1997. Experience with the engine now

The YF-22A's inlfight refueling reeceptacle is located on the aircraft's centerline, approximately midway between the cockpit and the exhaust nozzles.

Inflight refueling was utilized regularly during YF-22A testing to extend time in the air and thus allow test objectives to be achieved without interruption.

totals at over 3,000 hours of ground and air time. Some 1,500 of those hours include tests with two-dimensional exhaust nozzles.

The Pratt & Whitney YF119-PW-100 is a counter-rotating, dual rotor, augmented turbofan engine. The low-pressure rotor consists of a three-stage fan driven by a single-stage low-pressure turbine. The high-pressure rotor consists of a six-stage high-pressure compressor driven by a single-stage high-pressure turbine. High-pressure compressor exit guide vanes are cast as an integral part of the strutless diffuser. The exhaust system consists of a fully modulating cooled augmenter and a rectangular, two-dimensional, convergent-divergent nozzle with a thrust vectoring (TV) capability (plus or minus 20°). The flight control system commands the nozzle vector angle through the engine control system. Nozzle exit area and thrust vector angle are set by upper and lower divergent flaps which are each independently powered by a pair of hydraulic actuators. The engine is controlled by a redundant, engine-mounted full-authority digital engine control (FADEC) which interfaces with hydraulic actuators on the nozzle, fuel throttling valves, and compression system variable geometry. Hydraulic and electrical power for the control system is supplied by an independent engine-mounted hydraulic system and engine-mounted generator. The YF119-PW-100 is rated in the 35,000 lb. th. in afterburner class. Military power is approximately 23,500 lb. th. Production engines will differ from those utilized in the ATF prototypes only in having a slight increase in fan section diameter.

The General Electric YF120-GE-100 is a counter-rotating, dual rotor, variable-cycle, augmented turbofan engine. It is controlled by a triplex, engine-mounted, full-authority digital engine control unit (ECU). The low-pressure rotor consists of a two-stage fan driven by a single-stage high-pressure turbine. The variable cycle

technology enables the engine to operate as a conventional turbojet at supersonic speeds, while exhibiting the characteristics of a more fuel-efficient turbofan at subsonic cruise speeds. The nozzle is a two-dimensional convergent/divergent design with a thrust vectoring capability.

One of the primary low observables areas of concern was the F-22's exhaust system. In order to maintain the low observables objectives of the rest of the design, the exhaust system and associated empennage area were required to meet edge orientation and surface discontinuity specifications. Additionally, they were required to incorporate high-temperature technologies. These were required to provide broadband low observable performance without inhibiting the exhaust system's propulsion performance.

Fuel tanks are inerted using OBIGGS-generated nitrogen. An inflight refueling receptacle, which rotates into position upon pilot command, is located dorsally, at about the mid-fuselage point on centerline.

Weapons/Sensors: The Westinghouse/Texas Instruments radar is a very low observables active, electronically scanned array (ESA) antenna design that is integral with the aircraft radome and CIP. It is a multimode-capable unit and has a wide field of view. ADA software (with 800K lines of code) has been demonstrated. Some antennas, such as communication, navigation, and IFF are integrated into the airframe as conformal hardware and are integral with the aircraft's wing and vertical tail leading edges. Select antennas are multi-function and use shared assets to perform radar track warning, missile launch detection, and threat identification.

The technology Lockheed developed for the first control radar and other avionic apertures met the F-22's low observable requirements without impacting aperture performance. The integration of these apertures into a low observable vehicle is

critical to mission survivability.

Weapons are carried internally. There are two side bays positioned integral with the intake cheek assemblies each covered by a hydraulically actuated two-panel hinged door. These are optimized to carry a minimum of two AIM-9s each. Ventrally, there is a single main bay covered by a hydraulically actuated four panel hinged door. This bay is large enough to accommodate at least four AIM-120s. At a later date, as improved versions of extant missiles, or advanced missiles such as the *Have Dash 2* air-to-air missile or *Have Slick* air-to-surface missile, enter the inventory, they will be easily accommodate by the F-22's weapons bays.

The F-22A will be equipped with an improved General Electric M61 multi-barrel rotary gun mounted on the right side of the aircraft above and aft of the intake. Additionally, provision will be made to accommodate a variety of air-to-surface weapons as necessary.

General Dynamics has been tasked with providing dedicated versions of an advanced electronic warfare suite and a new communications/navigation/identification system. Both will be derived from integrated electronic warfare systems (INEWS) and integrated communications and navigations avionics technology.

Miscellaneous Systems and Subsystems: All avionics and miscellaneous subsystems on both the YF-22A and F-22A are purposefully located on the aircraft to permit ground level access for maintenance. A brass-board *Pave Pillar* avionics architecture was utilized and demonstrated. The following are components of the avionics suite:

Common Integrated Processing (CIP): The CIP utilized in the F-22 supports all signal processing, data process, digital input/output (I/O), and data storage functions using a single integrated hardware and software design. It is distinguished from federated or partially integrated architectures because it provides the requisite high-performance computing capability with lower installed weight, volume, power, and cost. This integrated architecture incorporates the *Pave Pillar* concepts and implements Joint Integrated Avionics Working Group (JIAWG) standards. These include the parallel-interface (PI) bus, the test-maintenance (TM) bus, and the data processing element (DPE) which employs a high performance 32-bit central processing unit (CPU) and the Intel 80960 reduced instruction set computer (RISC) processor. The 80960 instruction set architecture (ISA) is one of two 32-bit ISAs chosen by the JIAWG as the basis for standardization of 32-bit embedded avionics computers.

Air Data Systems: Both YF-22As are equipped with flight test nose booms which provide air data as well as AoA and side slip information to a special flight test cockpit display and the instrumentation package. The nose boom is totally inde-

External changes scheduled for the EMD F-22A (right) are visible in this computer image. Noteworthy are wingtip, horizontal tail, and vertical fin redesign, as well as revised nose and cockpit configurations.

pendent from the production low-observable pneumatic air data system (PADS). This system consists of two fuselage-mounted air data probes, one on each side of the fuselage located aft of the radome, and four flush-mounted static ports (two on each side of the fuselage) which also are located aft of the radome above and below the chine. Total pressure, static pressure, and AoA information are derived from the air data probes. The set of static pressure ports above the chine are used to measure angle of sideslip at low AoA and the lower set is used at high AoA. Air data computers convert the pressure inputs to electrical signals and correct for local flow effects.

The PADS provides air data to the flight control system (and other aircraft systems) within the conventional AoA. As AoA increases above approximately 33°, the flight control inputs transition from the pneumatic value to an inertially derived AoA. Pneumatic angle of sideslip is used up to much higher AoA until it too transitions to an inertially derived angle of sideslip above 60° AoA. At negative AoA the transition occurs at -5° and -20° respectively.

Vehicle Management System (VMS): The VMS consists of the following computer subsystems and their common bus interfaces: flight control computers and bus controllers; left and right engine control computers; head up display (HUD); integrated vehicle subsystem controllers; fuel management system; pneumatic air data system transducers (PADS); inertial navigation system (INS); mission display processors (MDP); and the integrated flight propulsion control (IFPC) 1553B buses. The VMS subsystems and their associated bus structure are flight-safety critical in nature with the exception of the MDP and its interface to the other aircraft avionics. For example, the pilot has no control over the engine except via the IFPC buses, and the FLCCs would not operate safely without the PADS. The IVSCs are required to turn on the emergency power unit in the event of a dual engine flameout or the simultaneous loss of the generators. The HUD provides the pilot with attitude and air data information in the event of loss of avionics and displays. The INS provides the aircraft velocity vector used by the flight control system in the computation of inertial AoA and sideslip angles when the aircraft is outside the range of the PADS as well as attitude information. In short, the VMS provides the pilot with everything needed to fly and land the aircraft safely under all recoverable failure situations.

Integrated Vehicle Subsystem Control (IVSC): The IVSC is part of the vehicle management system. The IVSC interfaces pilot commands to subsystems, communicates subsystem status to the pilot, and performs monitoring and control of certain subsystem functions. The IVSC also provides status, alerts, warnings, and diagnostics to assist the pilot in fault detection and corrective actions. These functions are accomplished for the following subsystems via the IFPC digital data bus, dedicated cockpit switches and lights, mission display processors, and multi-function displays (MFDs): landing gear system (IVSC controls retraction); 4,000 psi hydraulic system; environmental control system (IVSC controls); electrical system; auxiliary power system (IVSC partially controls); pilot's life support systems (IVSC controls); fire protection system (IVSC controls); master caution annunciation (IVSC partially controls); and cockpit controls and indicators as required for the above subsystems or functions (IVSC partially controls). The IVSC replaces all relay logic with software. It also reduces the number of dedicated displays, panels, and switches historically associated with each subsystem.

Artist's rendering of EMD F-22A. Changes include a shorter nose, a more forward cockpit location, truncated wingtips, and a revised horizontal tail configuration. Also noteworthy are smaller vertical tails.

Flight Test Instrumentation: Baseline flight test instrumentation requirements were apportioned in accordance with each prototype's planned flight test assignments. The system was designed with the flexibility necessary to permit some expansion, and as areas of concern were identified during flight test, limited additional instrumentation was added to support problem identification and resolution.

The measurements were transmitted to ground receivers via encrypted and unencrypted telemetry links. Specialized data also was acquired and recorded by dedicated systems. The instrumentation system acquired the following types of data: signals from dedicated flight test instrumentation transducers (approx. 50 accelerometers; approx. 260 strain gauges; approx. 150 pressure transducers; approx. 150 thermocouples; and approx. 15 position indicators); aircraft electrical signals (approx. 20); selected words from MIL-STD-1553 buses (approx. 100); HUD video; bulk data from MIL-STD-1553 buses; and armament system high speed photography (4 cameras).

The pulse code modulation (PCM) data acquisition system is a semi-distributed system with one master controller and a maximum of 24 remote signal conditioning/digitizing/multiplexing units. The remote units are able to accept analog and digital information. Under control of the master unit, two modules are capable, as passive listeners, of acquiring pre-selected MIL-STD-1553B data bus messages for inclusion with other PCM data. The PCM system has an integral time code generator. The central controller is programmable to provide flexibility for data frame formatting. PCM data acquisition is limited to information for which

a frequency response of 100 Hertz (Hz) is required. A passive system for recording bulk MIL-STD-1553B bus data also was installed. This system is capable of acquiring data from multiple buses. A small constant bandwidth frequency modulation (CBWFM) system also is used for high frequency engine data and weapons bay acoustic measurements. PCM data was encrypted for transmission to one or more ground monitoring facilities via telemetry link. The CBWFM data was transmitted in the clear.

Pratt & Whitney instrumentation information was in a RS-232 formatted Universal Asynchronous Receiver/Transmitter (UART) data stream. A special interface unit was designed and installed to convert the UART data stream to a PCM stream.

PCM, CBWFM, bulk 1553 bus and Pratt & Whitney engine data were recorded on a 28-track instrumentation tape recorder. A VHS format video recorder was installed to record HUD symbology and video information. Sixteen mm. cameras operating at 200 frames per second were installed to photograph weapon releases. Time correlation for the cameras was provided by recording the unmodulated IRIG "B" signal on the edge of the film. The cameras could be controlled manually by the pilot or automatically by the weapon separation signal.

A special flight test nose boom and high accuracy digital transducer was installed on, and in, the nose radome for the acquisition of free stream total and static pressures and AoA and sideslip. Nose boom indicated airspeed, pressure altitude, rate of climb, AoA, and sideslip were displayed in the cockpit on a special programmable CRT display.

Artist's rendering of NATF — which is the proposed Navy F-22. There is little commonality between this fighter and its Air Force sibling. Need for variable-sweep wing caused a major redesign of the entire aircraft.

YF-22A, N22YF, during flight test over Edwards AFB. Readily visible are weapons bay doors, landing gear well doors, and miscellaneous fairings for aileron actuators, ram air ducting and other systems. Noteworthy is extended full-span leading edge flap and tapered control surface inboard and outboard caps.

YF-22A, N22YF, turning final at Edwards AFB. Aircraft is equipped with anti-spin chute and associated mounting assembly. Spin chute height was determined in part by the exhaust efflux envelope of the vectorable nozzles. The nozzles and associated fairings differed between N22YF and N22YX as a result of the GE and Pratt & Whitney engine variations.

YF-22A, N22YF, the first prototype, on its final test flight became the only ATF prototype to achieve Mach 2. During testing at Edwards AFB, this aircraft logged 43 flights totaling 52.8 hours. As of this writing, it is being utilized as a systems mock-up and study tool at Lockheed's Marietta, Georgia facility.

LOCKHEED F-22

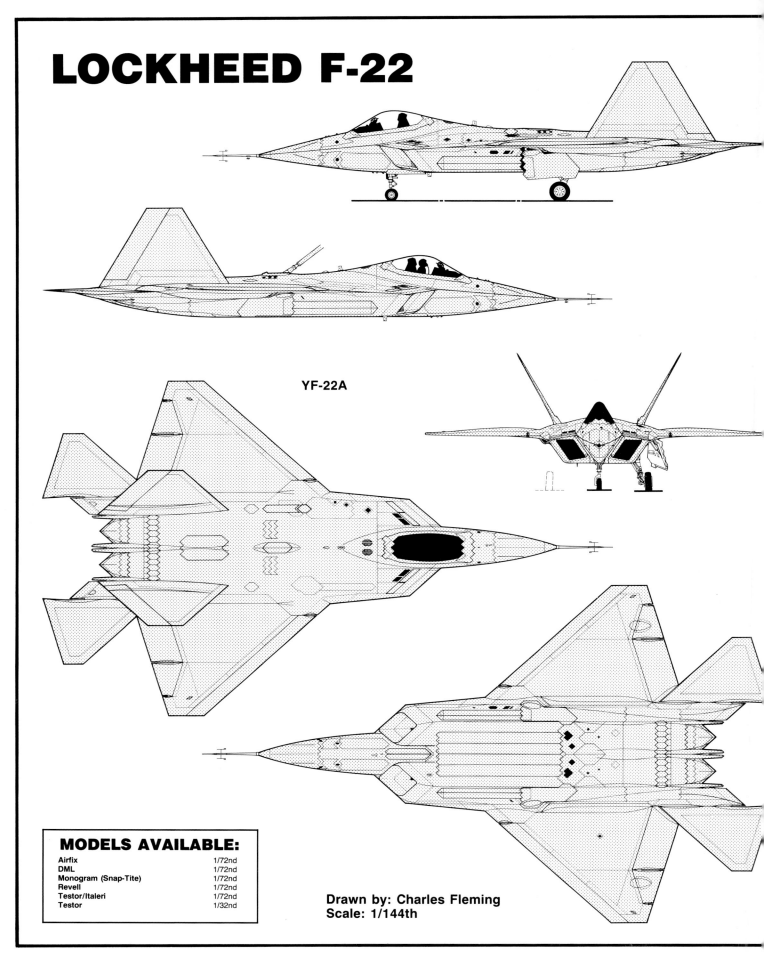

YF-22A

MODELS AVAILABLE:

Airfix	1/72nd
DML	1/72nd
Monogram (Snap-Tite)	1/72nd
Revell	1/72nd
Testor/Italeri	1/72nd
Testor	1/32nd

Drawn by: Charles Fleming
Scale: 1/144th

COLOR AND MARKINGS:

Color: Both prototype aircraft are painted in the same overall scheme; the upper radome and nose above the chine aft to the rear of the canopy, the outside surfaces of the vertical stabilizers, and the rudders are gray - F.S.36270. The remainder of the upper fuselage, the tops of the wings and stabilators and the inner surfaces of the verticals are dark gray - F.S.36118. The entire lower fuselage, including the nose, the bottom surfaces of the wings, and stabilators are all F.S.36375.

Markings: The Air Force star and bar insignia are conventionally stenciled. On the upper wings they are F.S.36270, while on the lower surfaces, they are F.S.36231. Both aircraft have three horizontal colored bands at the tips of the verticals. On the number one prototype, N22YF, starting at the top, they are red, white and blue. The blue stripe has an unbroken row of white stars from end to end. On the number two aircraft, N22YX, the red and blue are reversed with the blue (again with a row of stars) on top. On the number two aircraft, the stripes are repeated on the insides of the fin tips. Additionally on number one, there are full color TAC badges on the verticals and full color AFSC badges on the main gear doors. Just forward of the missile bay doors on the sides of the intakes are General Electric logos for the F120 engines, which were not selected. On the number two aircraft, the logos on the intake sides are for the winning Pratt and Whitney F119 engines. The badges for the F119 engine team was carried on the insides of the verticals.

PERFORMANCE AND SPECIFICATIONS:

Length (YF-22): 64 ft. 6 in. (19.65 m.)
Length (F-22): 62 ft. 6 in. (19.05 m.)
Wingspan (YF-22): 43 ft. 0 in. (13.1 m.)
Wingspan (F-22): 44 ft. 6 in. (13.56 m.)
Wing area: 840 ft.²
Wing leading edge sweep angle (YF-22A): 48°
Wing trailing edge forward sweep angle (YF-22A): 17°
Wing aspect ratio: 2.2
Horizontal stabilator area (YF-22A): 67 ft.² (6.22 m.²)
Vertical tail surface area (YF-22A): 109 ft.² (10.1 m.²)
Wing area (F-22A): 840 ft.² (78 m.²)
Wing leading edge sweep angle (F-22A): 42°
Wing trailing edge forward sweep angle): 17°
Horizontal stabilator area (YF-22): 67 ft.² (6.22 m.²)
Horizontal stabilator area (F-22): 68 ft.² (6.32 m.²)
Vertical tail surface area (YF-22): 109 ft.² (10.13 m.²)
Vertical tail surface area (F-22): 89 ft.² (8.27 m.²)
Height: 17 ft. 8.9 in. (5.39 m.)
Operating weight empty: 31,000 lb. (14,061 kg.)
Internal fuel weight: 22,000 lb. (9,979 kg.)
Normal takeoff weight: 58,000 lb. (26,308 kg.)
Max. speed mil. power: Mach 1.6 (1,059 mph/1,704 km/h)
Max. speed afterburner: Mach 2.2 (1,451 mph/2,335 km/h)
Max. g = 9, max. sustained g at Mach 1.8 = 6.
Service ceiling: 65,000 ft. (19,812 m.)
Takeoff/landing field length req.: 3,500 ft. (1,067 m.)
Unrefueled combat radius: 750 to 800 n.mi. (1,389 to 1,481 km.)

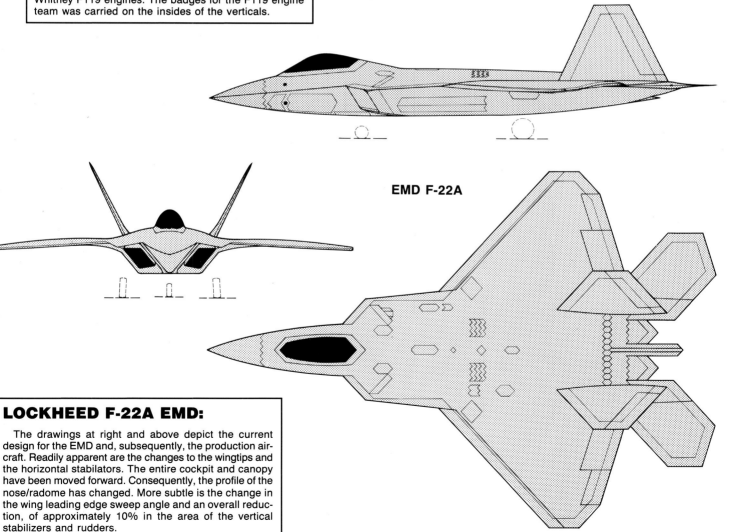

EMD F-22A

LOCKHEED F-22A EMD:

The drawings at right and above depict the current design for the EMD and, subsequently, the production aircraft. Readily apparent are the changes to the wingtips and the horizontal stabilators. The entire cockpit and canopy have been moved forward. Consequently, the profile of the nose/radome has changed. More subtle is the change in the wing leading edge sweep angle and an overall reduction, of approximately 10% in the area of the vertical stabilizers and rudders.

Lockheed

YF-22A, N22YX, during flight testing at Edwards AFB. APU exhaust (just to the left of centerline and aft of the wing leading edge/fuselage juncture), inflight refueling receptacle location, and exhaust nozzle variations are readily discernible. Noteworthy, too, is vertical fin tip marking variation from N22YF.

YF-22A, N22YX is distinguishable by comparing its vertical fin tip markings and the engine logo on the forward intake cheek. Scarcity of external protuberances is in concert with low observables emphasis. This is currently the only flying ATF prototype; the two YF-23s and the other YF-22 have been grounded.

Cockpit of YF-22A, N22YF. There will be many changes before this cockpit sees production, not the least of which will be the reversion to more conventional push buttons in place of the prototype's finger-on-glass (FOG) system. The quantity of CRT/MFD-type displays is unprescedented in a fighter-class aircraft.

Jay Miller/Aerofax, Inc.

EMD cockpit mock-up right console, originally for interior lighting and environmental systems controls, is now location of side stick controller with arm support.

Jay Miller/Aerofax, Inc.

EMD cockpit mock-up left console supports throttle quadrant levers and HOTAS. Control panel mounts switches for interior lighting, communication, and other miscellany.

Mock-up EMD F-22A cockpit. Raster-type HUD's large size is noteworthy, as are numerous MFDs. Center stick now has been abandoned in place of side stick controller.

Jay Miller/Aerofax, Inc.

YF-22A cockpit visibility is exceptional. Production aircraft probably will incorporate indium tin oxide as part of the laminate to lower the cockpit radar return.

Jay Miller/Aerofax, Inc.

Jay Miller/Aerofax, Inc.

Single-piece transparency of polycarbonate material is integral with canopy assembly. M-shaped piece at front is concession to low-observables technology.

YF-22A structure and surface design complexity is readily apparent in this view. Avionics are accessed via panel bearing F-22 logo. Note exceptional pilot visibility.

EMD F-22A COCKPIT

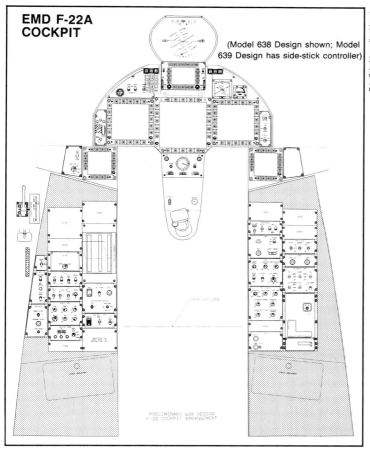

(Model 638 Design shown; Model 639 Design has side-stick controller)

PRELIMINARY 638 DESIGN
F-22 COCKPIT ARRANGEMENT

Eric Schulzinger/Lockheed

Cockpit of YF-22A, N22YX, has been modified for extended flight test program. Most visible change is in the form of the analog panel visible upper left. Main instrument panel is dominated by MFD-style CRT's. As shown, systems controls were via FOG. Throttle quadrant and landing gear extension/retraction handle are visible on left. Side-stick controller is visible on right. Rudder pedals, not visible, also are fly-by-wire. HUD, utilized in the prototype aircraft, is an interim unit and considerably smaller than the advanced raster-type now scheduled for production F-22A's. Overall cockpit design has been optimized to help reduce total aircraft radar cross-section. Heavy emphasis has been placed on panel configuration, placement, and materials selection. Production cockpit will return to more conventional push-button technology and some basic analog instrumentation.

Jay Miller/Aerofax, Inc.

Serrated radome edges are related to low observables requirements. Angled strips on right are static discharge lines. Discs on left are conformal static sensor ports.

Jay Miller/Aerofax, Inc.

Jagged edge delineates radome break line. Converging stripes are faired static discharge lines. Circular conformal static sensors will replace conventional units.

Jay Miller/Aerofax, Inc.

Chined nose design and related interfaces with other fuselage assemblies are all in response to radar cross section values. The YF-22A is designed to be very stealthy.

Jay Miller/Aerofax, Inc.

Avionics are accessed through removable panels on either side of nose, below and ahead of cockpit area. Noteworthy are serrated leading edge and angled rear edge.

25

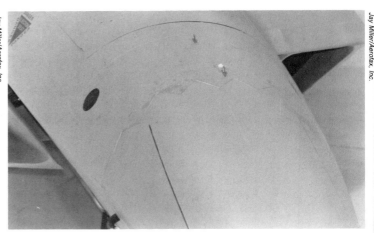

Serrations on panel edges do not delineate bay volumes underneath. Serrations usually are simply overlapping lips that reflect radar energy away from receiver.

Serrated radome interface edges indicate break line when radome is removed. Texas Instruments radar is assumed to be integral with firewall structure at breakpoint.

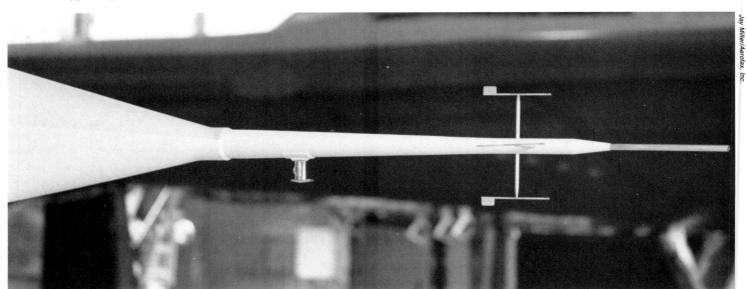

Status of pitot boom on production F-22 is unclear as of this writing, but it is presumed it will be either considerably smaller than the boom on the prototype aircraft (shown), or eliminated altogether. Prototypes both had booms serving not only conventional static needs, but also as mounting points for pitch and yaw vanes.

Little has been released describing the joint venture Texas Instruments/Westinghouse ATF radar and its very low observables active, electronically scanned array antenna.

Intake and cooling vents for avionics bays and other systems are found in various positions. Where necessary, these are covered with low observables mesh.

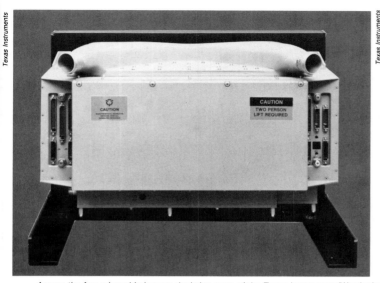

Among the few releasable images depicting parts of the Texas Instruments/Westinghouse radar and associated systems are these depicting the mission/display processor. Typical of state-of-the-art equipment of this type is the density of high-capacity solid state electronics and an associated high-capacity cooling system (top).

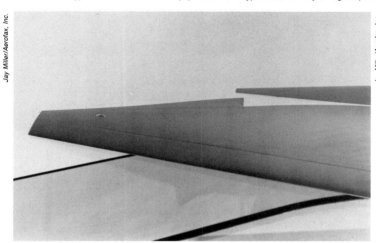

YF-22A wing is a highly complex structure built primarily of composites. Complexity of computer-generated compound curves and wing twist is subtle.

Each wing is equipped with a full-span leading edge flap (carried to the wing tip), a conventional aileron, and a conventional single-piece trailing edge flap.

Wing compound curvature and twist is evident when trailing edge is compared to leading edge. Note full-span leading edge flap and special inboard end cap. Leading edge surfaces are programmed to function as a result of airspeed, altitude, and angle-of-attack via control system computers.

Blending of YF-22A wing/fuselage interface was complicated by compound curvature of wing upper surface. Close tolerances of articulated surfaces such as wing leading edge flap, trailing edge flap, and aileron, dictated by low-observables requirements, compounded difficulties. Construction materials are primarily composite.

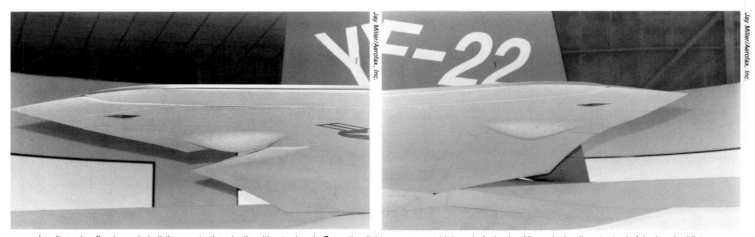

Leading edge flap is carried all the way to the wingtip without a break. Formation lights are recessed inboard of wingtip. Aileron hydraulic actuator is faired under blister. Compound curve of wing trailing edge is readily apparent in this view, as is notch in flap inboard cap providing horizontal stabilator clearance.

Empennage area between vertical tails is optimized for low drag while accommodating needs of the articulated exhaust nozzles. Special fairings optimized for low radar return also have been developed. Vertical tail root sections are thickened to meet volumetric requirements of rudder actuators and electronic warfare systems.

The primarily composite construction vertical tail surfaces of the YF-22A are inordinately large as a result of the close coupling of the various lift and control surfaces and the aircraft's maneuverability requirements. Vertical surface area will be reduced on the production aircrft. Noteworthy is wing trailing edge.

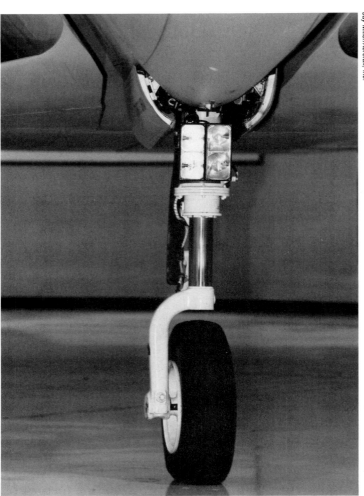

Nose landing gear is a simple configuration optimized to fit tight nose gear well dimensional constraints. Noteworthy are four-beam taxi light and small well doors.

Nose landing gear is manufactured by Menasco. Retraction is aft via hydraulic actuator. Size of nose landing gear well doors and tight tolerances is noteworthy.

Steerable nose gear is simple, yet robust. Anti-torque scissor link is mounted conventionally. Retraction tolerances, resulting from space constraints dictated by the forward fuselage design, are significant; gear alignment during the retraction process is critical. Constraints were dictated by low-observables requirements.

Aft nose gear retraction sequence is somewhat unusual. Forward retraction is preferred in order to take advantage of aerodynamic loads in event of emergency.

Main gear retract forward. Gear wells are covered by single piece doors which are closed and opened by a single, sequenced, independent hydraulic actuator for each.

Main gear strut assemblies are designed to accommodate the relatively heavy gross weights the F-22A will see in operational service.

Main landing gear well doors are lightweight structures with design considerations that include low-observables requirements. Noteworthy is serrated forward edge.

Left main gear well sans door assembly. Noteworthy are fuel, hydraulic, and pneumatic line systems, main gear actuator, and wing spar carry-through structure. Placement of hydraulic and pneumatic equipment in the well permits easy access. Slight forward cant to main gear strut assemblies is discernible.

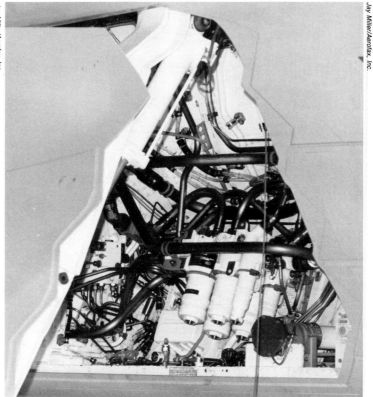

Design of main gear well door leading (and other) edges makes penetration and thus reflection of electromagnetic radiation difficult. Such attenuation reduces radar returns.

High pressure pump assemblies are located in the gear wells for easy access. Fuel, pneumatic, and hydraulic lines all run through the main gear well areas.

Main gear tires are Michelin Air Xs. The metal wheel design and assembly is conventional. Each main gear is equipped with a multi-disc brake inboard of the wheel. A large anti-torque scissor link assembly which angles inboard and forward maintains accurate tire track. The shock strut is integral with the main gear strut assembly.

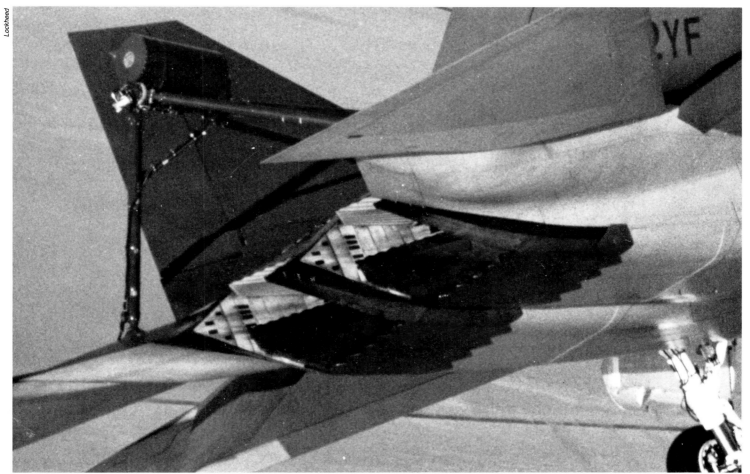

YF-22A, N-22YF, was fitted temporarily with a spin recovery chute and associated mounting assembly during the course of spin tests conducted during the flight test program. The chute could be ballistically deployed from its can-like container and would rapidly stabilize the aircraft if spin recovery proved difficult.

During ground tests of the spin recovery chute it was found to perform flawlessly. Tether length was in excess of 100 ft. Ballistic deployment was accommodated by a pyrotechnic device that literally blew the canopy and associated riser assembly into the slipstream. The chute was not required during the spin test program.

The spin recovery chute and its associated mounting assembly created a slight drag penalty, but not enough to affect the results of the YF-22A spin test program.

Intake design is critical to maintenance of low-observables objectives View of YF-22A model reveals complex geometry of intake configuration.

Differences in intake placement philosophies between the Lockheed YF-22A and the Northrop YF-23A are evident in this side-by-side comparison. Northrop positioned their intakes ventrally under the wing leading edge chine. Lockheed utilized cheek mounted intakes. Both configurations met RCS specifications.

The blended wing/body design of the YF-22A contributes to structural efficiency and permits high internal fuel capacity. The wedge-shaped inlets are fixed ramp designs providing low airflow distortion and high recovery. In concert with low-observables objectives, they provide 100% line-of-sight blockage to the engine faces.

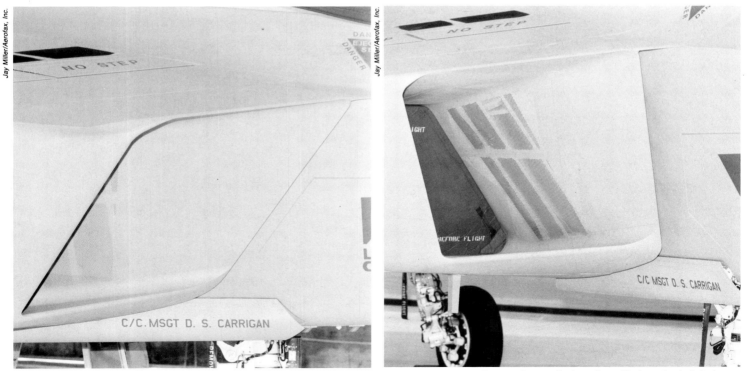

The fixed ramp intakes have no moving parts but are equipped with extensive boundary layer bleed systems. Because they are fixed, maximum Mach number is limited. The intake tunnels are S-shaped in order to all but eliminate radar returns from the engine compressor faces. Airflow distortion was a major design factor.

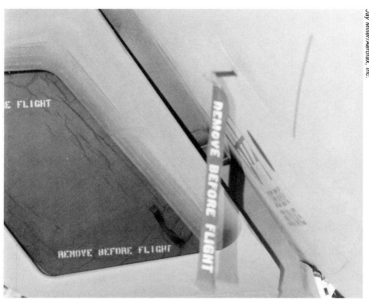

Each intake is offset from the fuselage to permit boundary layer bleed.
Inside the slotted area is a bleed intake which dumps boundary air overboard.

There were a number of significant exhaust nozzle differences resulting from the General
Electric F120 (shown) and Pratt & Whitney F119 engine installations.

A Pratt & Whitney F-119 static test article. Vectored thrust capability is amply illustrated by visible exhaust gases during full afterburner operation. Articulated nozzle flaps
serve to direct exhaust in concert with computer-generated control inputs. Such capability greatly improves maneuverability.

The Pratt & Whitney F119 engine is rated in the 35,000 lb. th. class at sea level. For the F-22 program, it is equipped with a two-dimensional vectorable thrust exhaust nozzle. Thrust vectoring capability is from plus 20° to minus 20°. Thrust vectoring is a capability integral with computer-generated control inputs.

Pratt & Whitney has logged well over 3,000 hours of static ground test and air time on the F-119 engine as of this writing and to date, difficulties have been minimal. Complexity of vectorable thrust nozzle assembly is accentuated by the fact it makes up approximately one-third the total engine length.

PRATT & WHITNEY F119
"THE NEXT GREAT FIGHTER ENGINE"
CONFIGURED FOR THE
LOCKHEED YF-22 AIRCRAFT

Pratt & Whitney's winning F119 turbofan engine design competed with General Electric's F120 for the ATF contract. Both propulsion systems represent state-of-the-art engine technology and are capable of very high thrust-to-weight ratios. Constructed of advanced, light weight alloys, it will become the world's first production engine with thrust-vectoring.

General Electric's ATF powerplant submission was the F120. A prototype YF-22A-optimized engine, possibly identified as EV88002, is seen being statically tested. Like the F119, it was equipped with a vectorable exhaust nozzle assembly. And like the F119, the F120 was rated in the 35,000 lb. th. class at sea level.

The YF-22A's inflight refueling receptacle is dorsally mounted on the aircraft centerline. It rotates into position upon pilot command. Because of its innate stability, the YF-22A was found by pilots to be docile in the inflight refueling mode. This capability was utilized repeatedly throughout the flight test program.

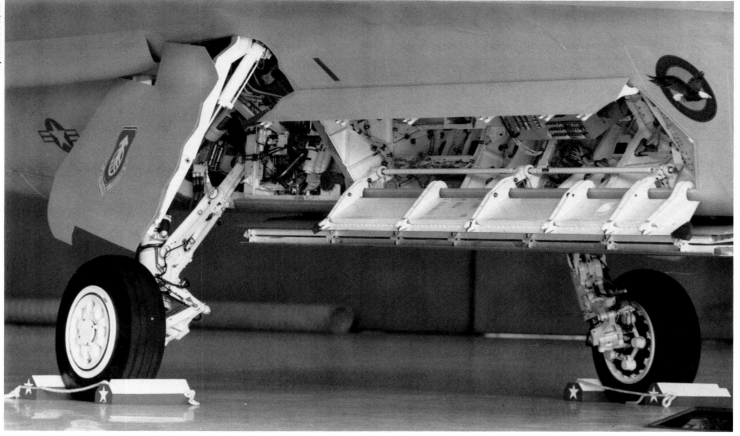

The YF-22A's are equipped with three large weapons bays. One is mounted on each side of intake cheek area, just ahead of the main landing gear wells, and a third, which is larger than either of the other two is mounted ventrally on the aircraft centerline. The bays provide ample room for carriage of all weapons internally.

On November 28, 1990, during the YF-22A Dem/Val program, an AIM-9 was launched successfully from N22YX's port weapons bay. General Dynamics' Jon Beesley was pilot.

On December 20, 1990, an AIM-120 was launched from N22YX, utilizing the ventral centerline weapons bay. Lockheed's Tom Morgenfeld was pilot.

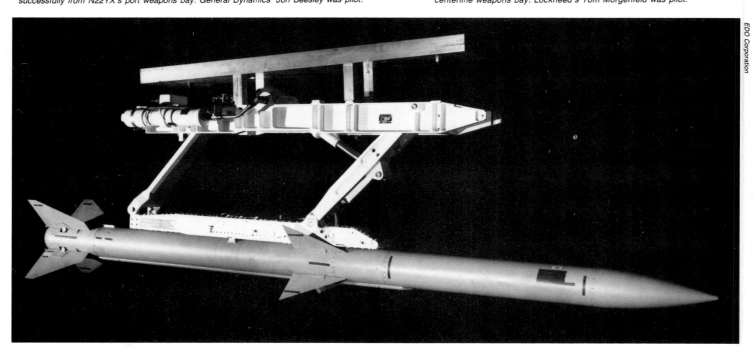

EDO Corporation's dedicated AIM-120 launcher is accommodated in the F-22's ventral bay only. Up to four AIM-120s can be fitted in the ventral bay. At launch, the accordion-like bay doors, of which there are four in two hinged pairs, open in unison. Sequenced extension of the launcher then exposes the missile for firing.